ISO 9001
in Plain English

Other Paton Professional books by Craig Cochran:

Customer Satisfaction: Tools, Techniques, and Formulas for Success
The Continual Improvement Process
Becoming a Customer-Focused Organization

Order these and other titles online at *www.patonprofessional.com*

ISO 9001
in Plain English

Craig Cochran

PROFESSIONAL

Paton Professional
Chico, California

Most Paton Professional books are available at quantity discounts when purchased in bulk. For more information, contact:

Paton Professional
A division of Paton Press LLC
P.O. Box 44
Chico, CA 95927-0044
Telephone: (530) 342-5480
Fax: (530) 342-5471
E-mail: *books@patonprofessional.com*
Web: *www.patonprofessional.com*

12 11 10 09 08   5 4 3 2 1

ISBN-13: 1-978-1-932828-20-7

Library of Congress Cataloging-in-Publication Data
Cochran, Craig.
ISO 9001 in plain English / Craig Cochran.
p. cm.
Includes index.
ISBN-13: 978-1-932828-20-7
1. ISO 9001 Standard. 2. Quality assurance—Standards. 3. Production management—Quality control—Standards. I Title.
TS156.6C63 2008
658.4'013—DC22
　　　　　　　　　　2008012843

Staff
Publisher: Scott M. Paton
Editor: Laura Smith
Book design: David Hurst
Cover: Caylen Balmain

To Muriel, a model of patience and love.

True intelligence
is taking something complex
and making it simple.

Craig Loch

Acknowledgments

I would like to offer my special thanks to the following people for their assistance in the development of this book: Muriel, Brynn, and Cullen Cochran; P.C. and Linda Cochran; Dr. Brett Saks, Kim Saks, and Aaron Saks; John and Rocio Lancaster; Mrs. Thelma O'Dell; Rosemarie Kobau; Scott Paton, Laura Smith, Heidi Paton, Christel Whetstone, and Tia Cronin; Jill Cooper; Aimee Seigler; David Levy; and Ufuk Taneri.

Contents

Chapter 1

Introduction

I am often asked, "Why is ISO 9001 so confusing?" What a great question! Could it be pure sadism and cruelty on the part of the authors? Probably not. A better explanation is that the standard was written to apply to any kind of organization. When you write a document that is applicable to everyone, you end up with something that's not very well suited to anyone. Another problem is that ISO 9001 was written by committee. There were a lot of hands stirring the pot, so the resulting standard is more complex than it would be had it been the work of a single person. Regardless of the reason why, the end result is that ISO 9001 is difficult to comprehend for people who do not completely immerse themselves in the document. I've spent many years immersing myself in this standard to make it easier for everyone else. This book interprets ISO 9001 in plain English and provides some value-added guidance on how to approach its implementation. After reading this, you'll be well prepared to begin implementing or auditing the standard.

Let's start with some basics. ISO 9001 is an international quality management system (QMS) standard. It presents fundamental management and quality assurance practices that can be applied by any organization. Few practices in ISO 9001 would be considered world-class, but the requirements represent an excellent foundation of planning, control, and improvement for just about any enterprise. The disciplines of ISO 9001 lay the groundwork for other improvement models, such as Six Sigma, the Malcolm Baldrige National Quality Award criteria, and lean enterprise by providing the structure that enables these other initiatives to flourish. Without a QMS, organizations have little chance of sustaining any improvements their short-term initiatives may realize. I personally believe that ISO 9001 is a basic model for managing any enterprise. Don't let the word "quality" confuse you. ISO 9001 isn't just about quality control of product or about what the quality department or lab is responsible for. It's also not a handbook for the quality manager. It goes beyond what many people traditionally consider "quality." In fact, I avoid using the word quality in relation to the standard anytime I can get away with it. ISO 9001 is a management system standard, period. From this point forward, I'll simply use the term management system to refer to the QMS specified by ISO 9001.

ISO 9001 is clearer and less ambiguous than any of its predecessors, but it still sounds like an international team of lawyers wrote it. The ultimate goal of this book is to remove the confusion from the standard and make it clear to everyone.

ISO 9001 is generic; its requirements aren't specific to any one industry or organization type. It's been used by nonprofits, service organizations, military, and governmental organizations, as well as traditional manufacturing companies. As I mentioned earlier, this broad applicability is one of the reasons why ISO 9001 is so confusing.

Because it's generic, ISO 9001 is also quite flexible. In few places does it specify exactly what an organization must do. In most cases, the standard leaves a great deal of discretion to the organization in terms of how it will design its processes and procedures. This enables organizations to develop exactly what they need to ensure success, instead of just blindly following a standard. The drawback, of course, is that the organization has to customize its approach to ISO 9001 conformance. I've had more than a few clients tell me, "I just wish ISO 9001 would come out and say exactly what we need to do." Well, that's not the way it works. The organization must figure out the best way to meet the requirements, and this is both liberating and challenging.

Documentation has always been a hallmark of ISO 9001. Documentation includes such things as procedures, policies, work instructions, specifications, and other tools that formally communicate information. ISO 9001 doesn't specifically require much documentation. Instead, it leaves it largely up to the organization to determine the type and magnitude of documentation needed. When people say, "We have all these documented procedures because ISO 9001 requires it," they are usually mistaken. In fact, the best management systems are usually quite lean, including only as much documentation as absolutely needed. That last statement is worth repeating: *Have only as many documented procedures as you really need.* When the list of procedures is lean, people are more likely to understand them and use them.

ISO 9001 has a significant focus on two important entities: the organization's customers and its top management. Customers are critical because they're the reason for the organization's existence. Understanding their requirements, capturing their perceptions, and making improvements based on customer feedback are key themes of ISO 9001. Top management is also hugely important because very little significant action takes place within an organization without top management's blessing—especially improvement actions. That said, top management plays a huge leadership role in any ISO 9001 management system.

"Shall" is the operative word in ISO 9001. This word indicates a requirement wherever it appears. This can take a variety of forms, depending on the specificity of the requirement and the needs of the company. A "shall" can often be satisfied by communicating a requirement, developing a process, documenting a procedure, keeping a record, training personnel, inspecting a product, or any number of other controls. In many cases, ISO 9001 leaves it up to the organization to decide exactly how it will address each requirement. The "shalls" of ISO 9001 start in section 4 and continue through section 8. Materials outside of these sections—such as the introductory text at the beginning of the standard—are for guidance and illustration purposes only. This material is not auditable, and an organization is not expected to interpret it as requirements.

One of the most confusing things about ISO 9001 is its tendency to repeat itself. The standard will specify a requirement, then almost repeat it in the next section. For example, planning is presented as a requirement at least five times. Don't get frustrated with this idiosyncrasy; when the standard repeats itself, the organization is only expected to address one of the requirements unless they differ in intent and scope.

ISO 9001 is organized in a process model, so its requirements operate as an integrated process. Organizing the standard in a process model helps universalize it, since all enterprises ideally operate as a series of interrelated processes. The process organization of ISO 9001 is a gentle way of discouraging the rigid organizational silos of some companies, as many processes cut across traditional departmental boundaries.

Let's take a quick look at ISO 9001's introduction and eight sections. This will be the only mention of the introduction and sections 1–3 since they are only in the standard for guidance purposes and you don't have to implement them. Sections 4–8 will be covered in much detail in the remainder of the book since these include the "shalls" of the standard.

INTRODUCTION

0.1 *General.* Implementing a management system is a strategic decision, intended to drive the success of the organization. The design of the system must be tailored to the organization's needs.

0.2 *Process approach.* An organization is composed of linked activities—processes—that transform inputs to outputs. The requirements of ISO 9001 are organized as processes, with explicit connections from one process to the next.

0.3 *Relationship with ISO 9004.* ISO 9004 outlines guidelines for performance improvement. It is designed to complement ISO 9001, providing guidance on applying the requirements of ISO 9001 for maximum benefit. Organizations cannot be certified to ISO 9004, but they can use this guidance document for getting the most mileage from ISO 9001.

0.4 *Compatibility with other management systems.* ISO 9001 is aligned with the requirements of ISO 14001 since both address complementary management systems. Implementing one of these standards facilitates the implementation of the other.

SECTION 1

1   *Scope*

1.1 *General.* ISO 9001 is intended to be used by organizations that desire to enhance customer satisfaction and produce product that meets all requirements.

1.2 *Application.* ISO 9001 was written to apply to any organization, no matter what kind of product it produces or what kind of processes it employs.

SECTION 2

2   *Normative reference.* ISO 9000, the vocabulary and definitions standard, is the normative reference to ISO 9001. In theory, this means that the definitions it provides may be used to clarify and reinforce requirements in ISO 9001.

SECTION 3

3   *Terms and definitions.* The terms "supplier," "organization," and "customer" are used in ISO 9001. Organization is meant to represent the entity implementing the standard. Suppliers are whom they buy goods and services from, and customers are whom they serve.

SECTION 4

4   *General requirements.* This section includes a high-level summary of the entire standard. It also addresses two basic administrative processes: document control and record control. The requirement for having a quality manual is included here, too.

SECTION 5

5   *Management responsibility.* This is an interesting part of the standard because it focuses completely on top management. Without fully implementing section 5's requirements, it's next to impossible to effectively implement the other requirements of ISO 9001. Management responsibility sets the stage for all other management system processes.

SECTION 6

6   *Resource management.* Organizations utilize many types of resources, including capital, tools, equipment, facilities, communication, and people. This section of ISO 9001 requires that resources be determined, provided, and maintained. In addition, section 6 includes training requirements.

SECTION 7

7   *Product realization.* This section addresses the processes that convert resources into your goods and services. It's focused on production and the processes that support production, and it's the longest section in the standard. In short, product realization covers your reason for existing: to produce a product that meets customer requirements. After we create a product, we typically have to measure our results, which logically leads us to section 8.

SECTION 8

8   *Measurement, analysis, and improvement.* The essence of improvement is the
     ability to measure and analyze performance. Section 8 addresses the processes
     that drive improvement within an organization, including auditing, analysis
     of data, customer satisfaction, and corrective and preventive action. Effective
     implementation of this section delivers some of the biggest paybacks of imple-
     menting ISO 9001.

It would be tempting to implement pieces of ISO 9001, focusing only on those
requirements you think will deliver maximum value, but ISO 9001 is intended
to be a holistic management system. All the pieces are connected to one another,
and interdependencies exist in every section of the standard. The implementation
approach can be widely customized, but it will be difficult to implement only a
portion of ISO 9001 and still realize its full benefit.

Don't be intimidated by ISO 9001. It is a model for success that can be utilized
by any organization. The remainder of this book will help you understand how to
apply it in the smartest manner possible.

Chapter 2

ISO 9001 Section 4 Quality Management System

I SO 9001's requirements start in section 4. This section focuses on the management system's documents and records. It also includes some very general requirements that are clarified in more detail in other parts of the standard. The issue of ISO 9001 repeating itself quickly becomes evident in section 4.

4.1 GENERAL REQUIREMENTS

Clause 4.1, General requirements, summarizes ISO 9001's major requirements into a list. However, the overview is so generalized that it's not much help to those trying to understand the specifics. The first sentence of clause 4.1 summarizes the entire standard, and the lettered bullets following it provide a little more detail. To understand ISO 9001, you have to delve into the specifics that are beyond clause 4.1.

Define sequence and interaction of processes within the system

Nearly everything in clause 4.1 is mentioned in more detail later in the standard. Two notable requirements are 4.1 a. and b., which require the organization to identify the processes within its system and determine their sequence and interaction. This can be accomplished in a number of ways. One of the simplest ways is to create a high-level flow diagram of the organization's processes, showing how the output of one process becomes the input to the next process. Make sure that both of the following process types are indicated:

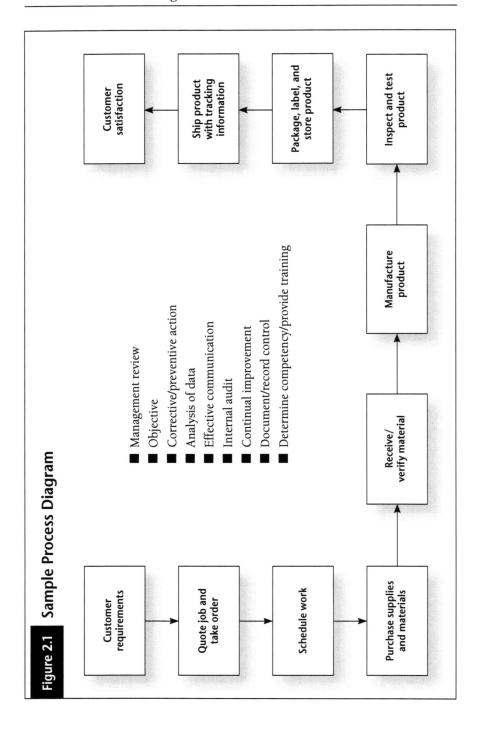

Figure 2.1   Sample Process Diagram

- Management review
- Objective
- Corrective/preventive action
- Analysis of data
- Effective communication
- Internal audit
- Continual improvement
- Document/record control
- Determine competency/provide training

Customer requirements → Quote job and take order → Schedule work → Purchase supplies and materials → Receive/verify material → Manufacture product → Inspect and test product → Package, label, and store product → Ship product with tracking information → Customer satisfaction

■ Core business processes specific to the organization
■ System processes required by ISO 9001 (e.g., document control, corrective action, and management review.)

The core business processes will have a fairly obvious flow to them, but the system processes required by ISO 9001 will have a less obvious flow. Many of them (document control, training, and corrective action, for example) are applied at any step of the process, as needed. Get creative with the process diagram, but try to keep it as simple as possible. (See figure 2.1.)

Another way to define the sequence and interaction of your processes is through a process matrix. A process matrix defines all the key processes of an organization in the left-hand column. Horizontally from left to right, it defines details for each process. These details typically include process owner, activities, inputs, outputs, customers, documentation, and measures of effectiveness. The benefit of a process matrix is that it adds valuable detail to the description of processes. The drawback is that it's less graphic and less able to illustrate process flow. There are other ways to describe your processes, but no matter which one you use, the output of this activity must appear in the quality manual, which we'll talk about in more detail later. (See figure 2.2 on page 10.)

Control over outsourcing

Another notable aspect of clause 4.1 is that it requires identification and control over outsourced processes. Outsourcing is not mentioned anywhere else in the standard, but it can affect the conformity of your products. You must identify outsourced processes and establish control over them. This is often done as a part of purchasing, which is described in clause 7.4.

The general nature of the ".1" clauses

It's worth noting the nature of the clauses of ISO 9001 that end in ".1." These include 4.1, 5.1, 6.1, 7.1, and 8.1. All of these function like overviews of everything that will appear in that section of the standard. These clauses are the source of much of the repeated requirements in ISO 9001, and they generally don't provide much useful information on their own.

Figure 2.2   Sample Process Diagram—ACME Inc.

Process	Activities	Inputs	Outputs	Customer(s)	Process documentation	Criteria
1. Sales	■ Provide specifications ■ Prepare quotes ■ Answer customer inquiries ■ Take orders ■ Review orders ■ Send to scheduling	■ Sales literature ■ Pricing schedules ■ Customer needs ■ Print	■ Customer orders ■ Clearly defined requirements	■ External customers ■ Scheduling ■ Manufacturing	■ OP-001 ■ Sales order form	■ Revenue growth ■ Net income growth
2. Scheduling	■ Prioritize orders ■ Maintain stock levels ■ Combine jobs in order to maximize efficiency ■ Publish manufacturing schedule ■ Amend schedule	■ Customer orders ■ Manufacturing capacity ■ Feedback from all functions	■ Manufacturing schedule	■ Manufacturing ■ Shipping ■ Receiving	■ OP-002	■ % on-time delivery to customer ■ Manufacturing efficiency
3. Purchasing	■ Qualify suppliers ■ Monitor supplier performance ■ Process purchase orders ■ Maintain approved supplier list ■ Improve supplier performance	■ Requirements from all functions ■ Pricing information ■ Historical supplier performance	■ Purchased product ■ Data on supplier performance	■ All functions of ACME	■ OP-003 ■ Purchase order form	■ % on-time delivery ■ Net income growth
4. Receiving	■ Verify incoming product ■ Stage materials in	■ Product requirements on purchase orders	■ Conforming products	■ All functions of ACME	■ OP-004 ■ Receiving ticket	■ Manufacturing efficiency

Process	Activities	Documents	Outputs	Customers	Procedures	Metrics
	■ warehouse ■ Communicate status to purchasing ■ Process nonconforming products, as needed	■ Purchased products	■ Records of incoming inspection			■ No loss time accidents ■ Net income growth
5. Manufacturing	■ Machining parts ■ Reflow ■ Hand insert ■ Assembly ■ Wash ■ Inspect & test	■ Production schedule ■ Product specifications ■ Purchased supplies & materials	■ Final product ■ Test data	■ External customers ■ Shipping	■ OP-005 ■ OP-006 ■ OP-007 ■ OP-008 ■ OP-009	■ % on-time delivery ■ Manufacturing efficiency ■ No loss time accidents ■ Net income growth
6. Shipping	■ Packaging products ■ Labeling ■ Preparing test data with shipping ■ Scheduling trucks ■ Shipping to customers ■ Monitoring shipments	■ Production schedule ■ Final product ■ Shipping supplies	■ Shipped product ■ No damage	■ External customers ■ Manufacturing	■ OP-010 ■ OP-011	■ % on-time delivery ■ No loss time accidents ■ Net income growth
7. Document & record control	■ Control documents ■ Ensure accessibility ■ Ensure periodic review of documents ■ Maintain records	■ Document control procedure ■ Record control procedure	■ Valid documents ■ Accessible records	■ All functions of ACME	■ OP-012 ■ OP-013	■ Internal audit results
9. Training & development	■ Assist in determining competency requirements ■ Provide training ■ Evaluate effectiveness ■ Develop new training	■ Competency requirements ■ Gaps in personal competency ■ Training checklists	■ Increased skills, knowledge, understanding ■ More effectiveness	■ All functions of ACME	■ OP-014 ■ Job descriptions	■ Internal audit results

(continued)

Figure 2.2   Sample Process Diagram—ACME Inc. *(continued)*

Process	Activities	Inputs	Outputs	Customer(s)	Process documentation	Criteria for success
	■ Administer OJT program ■ Administer new employee orientation ■ Maintain records		■ Records of training			
10. Management review	■ Analyzing data ■ Discussing issues ■ Determining actions & decision	■ Data ■ Information ■ Ideas ■ Problems ■ Opportunities	■ Actions ■ Decisions ■ Improvements ■ Management review records	■ All functions of ACME	■ OP-015	■ Revenue growth ■ Net income growth ■ Internal audit results
11. Improvement processes	■ Corrective action ■ Preventive action ■ Objectives ■ Customer satisfaction ■ Internal auditing	■ Customer feedback ■ Data ■ Trends ■ Nonconformities ■ Opportunities	■ Improvement ■ Customer loyalty ■ Long-term success	■ All functions of ACME ■ External customers	■ OP-016 ■ OP-017 ■ OP-018 ■ OP-019	■ Revenue growth ■ Net income growth ■ Internal audit results

FREQUENTLY ASKED QUESTIONS

Where is the requirement in ISO 9001 that says we have to follow our own procedures?

There is no specific requirement in ISO 9001 that states this. The expectation is that if you write a procedure within the scope of the management system, then you have committed to implementing it.

Do we have to implement every section of ISO 9001 in every department of our organization? As an example, I'm not sure how we'll implement the customer satisfaction requirements in our warehouse.

You must implement every *applicable* section of ISO 9001 in every department. Customer satisfaction, for instance, is often carried out by a marketing or customer service function. If your warehouse has no role in collecting or analyzing customer feedback, then it would make no sense to try to implement this requirement in that department.

4.2 DOCUMENTATION REQUIREMENTS

Before we go much farther, it's important to clearly understand the difference between a document and a record. The words "document" and "record" are sometimes used interchangeably, but they represent very different things. Not only are they different, but the controls applied to them are different, too. First, let's agree on what they are.

What is a document?

A document is a living thing. The information contained within a document is subject to change and can be revised. In fact, if an organization is really using its management system, documents will be frequently revised. Documents often tell people what they need to do or what requirements a product must meet. Any time you encounter information that guides activities on a forward-looking basis (i.e., now and in the foreseeable future), you're most likely dealing with a document. The control of documents typically revolves around who approves them, how they are made accessible to employees, and how they are updated, among other concerns.

What is a record?

A record, on the other hand, is history. The information on a record can't be changed, because the record simply states what has already happened. Records are used to provide proof that activities and products match requirements. They also provide the raw material for problem solving because they often detail the conditions and variables related to processes, such as equipment and materials used, time, date, location, and personnel. The control over records typically revolves around where they are kept, who is responsible for them, and how long they are maintained.

Some things start out as a document (such as a checklist or blank form) and become a record as information is written or typed into it. In other cases, things may exhibit characteristics of a document and a record simultaneously. Examples of these hybrids include work orders, sales orders, and purchase orders (to name just a few). All exhibit characteristics of a historical record and a live document. In these cases, the item is treated as a document until its real-time informational value has been exhausted. At that point, it's treated as a record.

Clause 4.2, Documentation requirements, is simply a section header. The meat comes in subclause 4.2.1.

4.2.1 General (documentation requirements)

Subclause 4.2.1 outlines the minimum documents required to establish ISO 9001 conformance. This is very helpful, since people often struggle with what they should document. Keep in mind that what's mentioned in subclause 4.2.1 are the minimums, and most organizations find that they need additional documentation to have effective control over their processes. I once assisted a company with two employees achieve ISO 9001 certification; despite its size, it required more documents than the minimum.

Documents required by ISO 9001

There are three documents explicitly required by ISO 9001 and six documented procedures. The three documents you must establish are:

■ Quality policy (clause 5.3)
■ Quality objectives (subclause 5.4.1)
■ Quality manual (subclause 4.2.2)

These are foundational documents that set the direction for the entire management system. We'll describe them in more detail when we come to the sections of ISO 9001 that explicitly address them.

The six procedures that require documentation are:

- Document control (subclause 4.2.3)
- Record control (subclause 4.2.4)
- Internal audit (subclause 8.2.2)
- Control of nonconforming product (clause 8.3)
- Corrective action (subclause 8.5.2)
- Preventive action (subclause 8.5.3)

These topics must be documented, but they don't have to constitute separate documents. For example, the topics of corrective action and preventive action are often combined into a single document. The important thing is to address those subjects in the clearest and most concise manner possible.

Documents beyond the minimum requirements

ISO 9001 requires that you have any documents necessary to maintain effective operation and control. Additional documents are determined by the organization based on its specific needs. The decision to have or not to have a document can be balanced by issues such as the training and skills of employees, the amount of supervision, and the nature of the organization's tasks. In general, it's best to keep your documentation as streamlined as possible. The more documentation you have, the less likely your personnel are to understand it. In any case, the amount of documentation beyond the required documents is for the organization to decide.

When ISO 9001 uses the term "documented procedure," it's referring to a written procedure (either hard copy or electronic) that addresses a particular activity or process. When ISO 9001 simply uses the term "procedure," it's simply referring to an agreed-upon method that's applied in a consistent manner. It's up to the organization to decide if the procedure must be documented.

The "D" words

There are three notable "D" words in ISO 9001: define, describe, and determine. To define, describe, or determine anything consistently, a document is probably going to be involved. Whenever you see these words in the standard, carefully consider documenting the subject that they address. Likewise, when ISO 9001 requires that a procedure be established, the organization should strongly consider documenting that procedure so it's communicated consistently.

FREQUENTLY ASKED QUESTION

Do we have to map all of our documents to ISO 9001 requirements?

No, not unless you see value in this. Some companies do this to demonstrate how they meet the various sections of ISO 9001, but it's certainly not a requirement.

4.2.2 Quality manual

Subclause 4.2.2 describes the requirements for the quality manual. The quality manual is a high-level description of the organization's management system. It typically provides a roadmap to where all the pieces of the management system are located, and it makes commitments to meeting the standard's requirements. Most quality manuals don't include a great deal of specifics, but rather point to other documents and procedures where the specifics reside.

ISO 9001 requires that four explicit considerations be included in the quality manual:

■ *The scope of the system.* The scope is a statement of the functions or departments included in the system. If a function is included in the scope, two things will happen:

☐ The function will be expected to implement all applicable requirements of ISO 9001. The key word is "applicable." This doesn't necessarily mean that the shipping department has to develop its own system for gauging customer satisfaction.

☐ The function must be audited sometime during the normal cycle of internal and external audits. The more specific the scope statement, the better. Ambiguities will only lead to trouble down the road. Here's an example of a reasonably written scope statement: "The scope of the ACME Inc.'s quality management system includes the sales, manufacture, testing, warehousing, distribution, and servicing of all widgets and doo-dads produced at the Marietta, Georgia, facility."

■ *Exclusions and their justifications.* Exclusions are simply requirements from ISO 9001 that do not apply to the organization and which the organization does not intend to fulfill. Exclusions can only be taken from section 7 (product realization) of ISO 9001. An organization could not exclude a requirement from section 5, regardless of what it considers to be the justification. I once had a customer tell me, "My top management is not very smart, so we need to exclude section 5 of the standard." Nice try, but you can only take exclusions from section 7.

Exclusions can only be taken when the organization does not perform the activity described in the requirement, and when this omission does not affect the organization's ability to supply product that meets all requirements. Exclusions cannot be made for "convenience" purposes. For example, many organizations would find it more convenient (at least in the short term) to exclude their design functions, but this is not permitted if design is taking place in the organization and it bears on the organization's ability to meet requirements.

Once an organization claims an exclusion in its quality manual, it must be justified. This means that the organization must explain the rationale for excluding the requirement. As far as I know, there's only one reasonable justification for excluding a requirement: The organization as described by the scope statement does not perform that activity.

Here is an example of an exclusion with the appropriate justification: "Design and development has been excluded from the quality management system because those activities do not take place at ACME Inc. All product designs are received directly from customers in the form of blueprints."

■ *Documented procedures or references to them.* ISO 9001 requires that the quality manual include the management system procedures or references to the procedures. Including all the procedures in their entirety would make for a very long and unwieldy quality manual. Some very small, simple organizations with few procedures find that it makes sense to include all their procedures right in their quality manual. This is a rarity, though. Most organizations simply refer to a different function of their management system: "For more information on document control, see document OP-001, Document Control Procedure." These references point the way to the detailed instructions that people use to make decisions and perform work. Keep in mind that the documented procedures that must be included or referenced in the quality manual are just the next level down in detail. You don't have to include all documents that comprise your management system.

■ *Description of the sequence and interaction of your processes.* This is a depiction of the major processes within your organization and how they fit together. It is often depicted as a flow diagram or other graphic, though it can be described in any way that makes sense to the organization. You may recall this requirement in clause 4.1 of the standard. The processes that you will depict fall into two basic categories:

　□ *Core processes that perform the work of the organization.* For example, if you're a widget manufacturer, these core processes might include stamping, grinding, polishing, and assembly. These processes are not mentioned by ISO 9001, but they're essential to your operation. You'll depict these processes and indicate how they fit together.

　□ *Management system processes mentioned by ISO 9001.* These include such things as training, management review, corrective action, and document control. These processes often don't have a sequence; they just happen where they need to happen. You'll need to show these on your process diagram, though they may be indicated outside the normal production flow.

Other items that could appear in a quality manual

The items required by ISO 9001 to be in the quality manual could easily be covered in a couple of pages. Many organizations elect to include additional items that add value to the quality manual. It's always a balancing act between keeping the quality manual a roadmap to more details and actually including details. Here are some of the elements that organizations often include in their quality manuals. However, they are not requirements:

■ Definitions or special terms unique to your organization
■ The quality policy
■ Identification of outsourced processes and some examples of how outsourced processes are being controlled
■ Explicit determination of who is "top management"
■ Explicit determination of who is the management representative
■ High-level organizational charts (typically included as an appendix)
■ High-level description of operations and/or documentation structure (typically included as an appendix)
■ Responsibilities and authorities of key personnel

I generally recommend that organizations not include specific objectives within the quality manual. The reason is that objectives are likely to change much more often than any other aspect of the quality manual.

Purposes of a quality manual

People often claim that their quality manuals don't serve much of a purpose. The truth is that they are quite general. Despite their general nature, they serve important purposes:

- Educate employees about the structure of the management system, its processes, and its broad intentions
- Define the system for third-party registrars
- Provide an initial basis for internal and external auditing
- Instill confidence in existing customers by indicating the organization's commitment to continual improvement and customer satisfaction
- Sell the organization to potential customers by revealing the organization's advantages over competitors
- Provide top management with a starting point for strategic planning and the development of key measures
- Guide middle managers in the development of functional/departmental systems and procedures
- Provide a road map to lower-level documents within the system

FREQUENTLY ASKED QUESTIONS

Why do most quality manuals include the same words as the ISO 9001 standard?

The purpose of this is to explicitly commit to everything in the ISO 9001 standard, which is something that most registrars require. There's no functional benefit to it, though. Something that might have functional benefit would be putting the intent of ISO 9001 into terms that organizational members understand.

Does everyone in our organization need to be familiar with our quality manual?

You must decide which documents of your management system are applicable to different personnel. The only universally applicable documents are the quality policy and quality objectives. Given the general nature of the quality manual, it's not likely that many employees would need to be very familiar with it.

4.2.3 Document control

Document control is one of the most basic disciplines in a management system. It's the process of making sure people have access to timely and accurate information to do their jobs. A document is anything in a fixed form that communicates customer requirements, guides decision making, or describes the correct way to carry out a process. This means that quite a few things that don't look like documents are in reality documents. These include printed e-mails, letters, memos, drawings, photographs, and even Post-it notes in some cases. Documents must be controlled or removed. Otherwise, mistakes are guaranteed.

Your procedure for document control must itself be documented. This is the first of the documented procedures required by ISO 9001. You will be expected to address all the individual requirements related to document control in your procedure. Do this as concisely and simply as possible. Document control is a process that many people within the organization will be exposed to, so it's important that the message be very clear.

Documents requiring control

"Do I need to control this document?" is one of the most frequently asked questions in organizations working toward, or maintaining, a formal management system. Given the universe of documents possibly requiring control, the question is understandable. Besides, most people would rather not control a document if they don't have to.

ISO 9001 provides a quick answer to the question of what must be controlled. The first sentence of subclause 4.2.3 on document control states, "All documents required by the quality management system shall be controlled." This means that if a document addresses or relates to any of the issues in ISO 9001, it must be controlled. Here are some questions to ask when determining whether a document should be controlled:

- Does the document guide the production of products (i.e., goods or services) provided by the organization?

- Does the document guide the verification, inspection, or testing of products provided by the organization?
- Does the document define customer and/or product requirements?
- Is the document used for controlling processes?
- Is the document used for decision making by personnel?
- Is the document used for collecting data that could be used later for decision making within the scope of the management system (e.g., a form)?
- Is the information on the document so critical that failure to keep it updated would pose a risk to the organization or its customers?
- Does the document address or relate to a requirement from ISO 9001?

If the answer to one or more of these questions is yes, then the document should be controlled. For illustration purposes, consider the following scenarios:

- An interoffice memo is posted on a wall in the fabrication department. The memo gives a number of functional and packaging requirements for a product that's fabricated there. Because of where the document has been posted and the information it contains, the memo should certainly be controlled. Ignore the fact that memos are rarely controlled; in this case, it provides customer requirements, guides decision making, and relates directly to ISO 9001 requirements. Even if the memo duplicates information contained elsewhere in controlled specifications, the uncontrolled memo would still be a problem. Eventually, there will be a discrepancy between the information in the memo and the information contained in the controlled specifications. The organization should either control the posted memo or get rid of it.
- A training department develops videotapes to train employees on the proper setup and operation of production lines. The videotapes are included in the training program for new hires and existing employees. In this case, document control is required because the tapes define process control, guide the production of products, and relate to the training requirements of ISO 9001.
- Product defect samples are displayed in a lighted glass cabinet in the visual inspection area. The samples illustrate the limits of various defects that can be considered acceptable to customers, and they're used when inspectors aren't certain of the criteria. Currently, the display cabinet is labeled "for reference only." Despite this declaration, the samples should be controlled because they define customer requirements.
- An organization develops a checklist that's used to record the results of product inspection. The blank checklist defines exactly what's to be inspected, as indi-

cated by the spaces that inspectors must complete. These blank forms need to be controlled as documents, and then as records once they're completed.

These scenarios highlight the fact that documents needn't be limited to traditional procedures, work instructions, and the like. The term "document" can encompass a wide range of things, all of which might require control, depending on the information they contain. Some examples include:

■ Electronic documentation
■ Photos
■ Drawings, diagrams, and sketches
■ Audio tapes and videotapes
■ Product samples and defect samples
■ Paint swatches for color matching
■ Checklists
■ Flow diagrams
■ Blank forms

Document vs. record

It's obvious from the foregoing list that controlling documents requires thinking of them as more than written procedures. However, before we jump into specifics, let's remind ourselves of the differences between a document and a record.

A document is a living thing. The information contained within it is subject to change; it can be revised. A record, on the other hand, is history. The information it contains can't be changed because it simply states what's already happened.

Now that we understand what documents are, let's explore the specific means of controlling them. By the way, one of the six documented procedures required by ISO 9001 is controlling documents, so whatever specific controls an organization decides upon must also be documented and controlled.

Approving documents

All documents must be approved for adequacy before being used. There are many ways to accomplish this. Paper-based documents often include spaces for authorized persons to sign or initial. Electronic documents can be approved through a typed name if passwords prevent anyone from falsifying the approval. In much the same way, e-mail can even be used. However, such approval should be visible to the user. Otherwise, the value of approval (i.e., as a cue that the document is OK for use) is lost.

Does the organization need to define who is authorized to approve documents? At least on a basic level, the answer is yes. A statement such as, "Documents must be approved by individuals responsible for managing the tasks described in the document" would satisfy the designation of approval authority. Alternatively, an organization may decide to be much more specific about who can approve documents. But from the titles shown beneath approval spaces, documents typically indicate who is responsible for approving them, and this self-declaration is usually adequate.

Note that a fine line exists between having too few and too many approvals on a document. For documents that cut across departments, the approval list should include all managers who are affected by the document. This provides buy-in and communicates to managers what's expected. The flip side is that obtaining eight or ten approvals can take a long time. Strive for the fewest number of approvals that will still provide buy-in for the information described in the document.

This buy-in can often be achieved by allowing personnel affected by a document to review it and provide feedback prior to its final approval. The review is a courtesy and a practical measure, and would only need to be recorded if the organization saw a necessity to do so.

Reviewing, updating, and re-approving documents

ISO 9001 introduces the requirement that documents must be reviewed, updated as needed, then re-approved. This doesn't mean routine document revision. The standard requires an organization to review documents periodically to see if they're still valid. If they are, the organization re-approves them. If they're not, either a revision is made or the document is declared obsolete. This prevents documents from becoming inaccurate or obsolete over time. If documents are used properly, this should never happen, but we all know that they're frequently ignored in the press of day-to-day work commitments.

What exactly triggers a document review? An organization can handle this in three ways:

■ Recall documents on a strictly periodic basis—every year, for instance—and review them, update as necessary, and re-approve them. This would certainly satisfy the standard. But it's sometimes difficult to review documents based strictly on the passage of time. This requires a fair amount of discipline because there's always something more important to do than reviewing documents. This system's success depends on the organizational skills of the person in charge of it.

■ Review, update as necessary, and then re-approve documents based on business triggers or real-world events that have the power to affect a document. Some examples include the introduction of new products, equipment, and processes; change in business focus; technological breakthroughs; and improved methods or practices. Because this approach is driven by actual events that make document review immediately relevant, it introduces a sense of urgency that's not present in the periodic approach.

If an organization decides to use this method, it needs to define the business triggers and responsibilities clearly in the document control procedure. The document administrator will typically monitor operations for these business triggers and ensure that the relevant documents are reviewed, updated as necessary, and re-approved. If a business trigger hasn't occurred within a reasonable period of time—say, three years—then documents should be recalled for review anyway.

■ Use the internal audit process to review documents. Keep in mind, however, that internal audits are sampling processes. By their very nature, they're only going to examine a representative sample of documents in existence. The standard implies that all documents must be reviewed. If an organization intends to use its internal auditing process to satisfy this requirement, then extra care must be taken when planning and scheduling audits to ensure that all documents are sampled during an extended period.

Identifying changes to documents

Documents must have revision changes identified. This is typically interpreted as the changes in the most current revision. Thus, if a document is on revision five, it will identify the changes that moved it from revision four to revision five. This identification assists document approvers to see what changed in the document, and it assists users in knowing what's changed so they can comply with the document's requirements.

Changes can be identified in a variety of ways, including:
■ Change logs at the end of documents
■ List of changes on the cover sheet
■ Underline, bold, italicize, or highlight changes throughout the document
■ Color coding of changes
■ Track changes within a word processing program

Identifying revision status of documents

Revision status simply indicates a document's most current revision. This is normally indicated by a revision number, letter, or date placed directly on the document. The revision status allows users to know whether they have the most current document. For paper-based documents, the revision status normally ties back to a master list or index that tracks the current revisions of all documents. For electronic documents, knowing the current revision is less important because the most current version is provided automatically to all users. Either way, the revision status must still be identified.

Making documents available at points of use

A document is useless if it's not accessible. ISO 9001 requires that "relevant versions of applicable documents are available at points of use." This means that current versions of documents must be accessible by the people who need them. It does not mean that everyone must have his or her own copy or computer terminal. If people know where the documents are located, have access to that location, and can make use of the information in the documents, then this requirement has been satisfied.

Some organizations develop elaborate schemes for distributing hard copy documents to different departments or functions. These often involve "acknowledgment of receipt" sheets that must be signed and returned with obsolete copies of documents. ISO 9001 doesn't specifically require such systems, though they may provide some value. Organizations must examine their own operations and decide what will provide the right balance of control and simplicity. Remember that the more bureaucracy involved, the slower the system will work and the more likely that users will attempt to circumvent it.

Making documents legible and identifiable

Legibility means that documents can be read and understood. They should be written in a clear, decipherable manner, in the language spoken by document users. For example, if a significant number of employees in a particular department speak and read in Spanish, then the documents would need to be legible to them. To do this, the organization could write the documents in Spanish or use graphic documents (e.g., photos or drawings) that can be understood regardless of the prevailing language. The organization could also employ bilingual personnel who are available to make the documents legible to those who can't speak the language in which the documents are written.

"Identifiable" simply means that documents have a title, document number, or other unique identifier that sets them apart from others. Organizations often develop document-numbering schemes that relate to the ISO 9001 numbering system. This is well intentioned but guaranteed to be obsolete in the future. Remember, ISO reviews and revises the 9000 series every few years, and this normally triggers a change in the way the standard is numbered. A better plan would dovetail with an organization's processes or departments. Such a system will be relevant to employees, and it won't become obsolete upon the next revision of ISO 9001.

Controlling external documents

An external document is published outside the organization and used within the scope of the management system. The eight questions listed at the beginning of this section will help determine if an external document should be controlled. Examples of external documents possibly requiring control include:

- Troubleshooting and/or calibration manuals published by equipment manufacturers
- Test procedures, specifications, and/or engineering drawings published by customers or other bodies
- Instructions, specifications, and/or procedures published by suppliers
- Standards published by industrial organizations applicable to the organization
- International standards such as ISO 9001

Once external documents have been determined, they must be identified, and their distribution must be controlled. Like internal documents, there must be a title, document number, or other unique identifier. Such identification typically comes from the source that publishes the document, and the organization simply adopts it.

Distribution control is important because most external documents arrive in paper form. Knowing where they're located is critical to controlling the information contained in them. For that matter, paper-based internal documents should also have their distribution controlled, but this isn't specifically required by ISO 9001. A distribution list simply defines the number of copies in existence and indicates where they're located. The copies are often numbered, and these numbers match the locations shown on the distribution list. When documents are revised, retrieving the old copies is much easier when their quantity and location is known.

Controlling obsolete documents

ISO 9001 imposes two controls related to obsolete documents: Their unintended use must be prevented, and they must be identified if they're retained. The easiest and most obvious way to prevent the unintended use of obsolete documents is to take them out of circulation. Simply round them up and remove them. This is quite easy when their exact locations are known. Controlling obsolete documents is one more good reason to maintain distribution lists for all paper-based documents, both internal and external.

Organizations often retain obsolete documents to preserve knowledge. These documents can be referred to when comparing, for example, a current process to one used five years ago. If an organization elects to retain obsolete documents, they must be identified by some means the organization considers suitable. This might include marking them as "history," "obsolete," "superseded," or "do not use," or putting them in a specially designated location that has controlled access. Whatever method is devised it must ensure that obsolete documents aren't floating around where they can be used improperly.

A few words on forms

The issue of controlling forms is a sore spot for many people. The resistance usually follows this general theme: "I just don't see the value in controlling forms. How are we supposed to do it, anyway?" The bottom line is that forms existing within the scope of ISO 9001—those that address a management system requirement applicable to the organization—undeniably require control. Why? Because the primary reason for a form is to create consistency in the way data are collected. This can only be enforced when everybody is using the same form, and this only happens through some type of document control.

Fortunately, forms are quite easy to control. Let's look at two different approaches, both of which are widely used by organizations:

■ *Forms controlled as "attachments" to procedures.* In this framework, forms are included within the procedure or documents that describe their use. (Must there be a procedure that describes the use of every form? Of course not, but it makes sense in some cases.) The forms are generally included as the last page or two of the procedure to which they belong. Approving a procedure can also include approving the form attached to it. The same goes for revising and identifying changes. The form is treated like another page of the procedure for control purposes, but it can be reproduced for use independently of the procedure.

When the form is revised, the procedure is also revised, and users are notified of the changes. The drawback of this system, of course, is that organizations are required to revise the entire procedure when the form is revised.

■ *Forms controlled individually.* In this framework, forms have individual numbers and revisions. Their approval may be made directly on the original copy or kept elsewhere, such as on a master approval sheet. The current revision of each form is usually indicated by a master list, computer index, or even by including it in a special file. When a form is revised, users are notified via memo, e-mail, or other means.

Forms are often printed in huge quantities, inevitably just before a minor change occurs that renders them obsolete. If the change was inconsequential, don't toss out the old forms. They can often be labeled with a disclaimer, "Previous versions of this form may be used." This will enable an organization to use the old inventory and avoid waste. Keep in mind that this only works when changes are minor and when the information conveyed does not seriously affect the organization's success.

Document formatting

Fortunately, ISO 9001 doesn't require any particular format for documents. An organization can decide for itself what format will work best. Furthermore, it's not required to stipulate a single type of format or style of document. However, a standardized format or style can be helpful in maintaining a consistent appearance for all documents. Many organizations stipulate only the content of document headers and cover sheets, while other companies require specific sections in each document, such as purpose, scope, responsibilities, equipment, and the like. Such decisions are up to the organization.

Whatever style and formatting though, the document control procedure should clearly define it. In fact, many organizations use their document control procedure as a guide for writing documents. In this way, the document control procedure does double duty by describing the control of documents and facilitating document development.

Summary

The basic tenets of document control are very simple. Most document control procedures can be drafted in four pages or fewer. Writing a document control procedure is easy: Simply work your way down the list of document control issues raised by ISO 9001 and describe what the organization is doing for each one. Keep it simple and avoid creating too much bureaucracy. An effective document control system will provide documents to users quickly and not slow them down with lengthy procedures.

FREQUENTLY ASKED QUESTIONS

We have different kinds of control for different types of documents. For example, our job procedures are handled differently from our product specifications. Is that OK?

Of course. Just make sure to address the different kinds of control within your document control procedure.

Do we need top management to approve all our documents?

I certainly hope not. There's nothing in ISO 9001 that requires top management to approve all documents. You decide who must approve documents.

We have a lot of job aids and work instructions in our work areas that are impractical to control. People use the information only occasionally. Can we just stamp all of this "For Reference Only"?

No. Either control the job aids and instructions, or get rid of them. Stamping something "For Reference Only" does little to prevent personnel from using the documents to guide their actions and make decisions.

4.2.4 Control of records

Most organizations retain hundreds, if not thousands, of records. They prove that the organization has done what it has committed to doing. As we described earlier, records are nothing more than history. Control of records is all about maintaining history so it can be retrieved when needed in the future.

Required records

The records that are specifically required by ISO 9001 are identified throughout the standard. Here are the records that you must control within your management system:

- Evidence of conformity to requirements and of effective operation of the QMS (clause 4.1)
- Management review records (subclause 5.6.1)
- Records of education, training, skills, and experience (subclause 6.2.2e)
- Records of the results of contract reviews and any actions taken (subclause 7.2.2)
- Design input records (subclause 7.3.2)
- Design review records (subclause 7.3.4)
- Design verification records (subclause 7.3.5)
- Design validation records (subclause 7.3.6)
- Design change records (subclause 7.3.7)
- Results of supplier evaluations and actions (subclause 7.4.1)
- Validation of (special) processes (subclause 7.5.2)
- Traceability records (subclause 7.5.3)
- Records of customer property that is lost, damaged, or unsuitable (subclause 7.5.4)
- Records of the basis for calibration when no standards exist (clause 7.6)
- Records of the results of calibration (clause 7.6)
- Internal audit records (subclause 8.2.2)
- Records of product conformity and product release (subclause 8.2.4)
- Records of the descriptions of nonconforming products and their dispositions (clause 8.3)
- Corrective action records (subclause 8.5.2)
- Preventive action records (subclause 8.5.3)

What constitutes control of records?

Just as with document control, you must describe your record control process in a documented procedure. The documented procedure must answer six questions for each record. These questions are most often addressed in a matrix of some sort, typically with the various records in the far left-hand column, and the details of control shown in the subsequent columns. The record matrix is the "meat" of the document, but it's also very helpful to show exactly how your organization defines each one of these words, particularly where the word can have more than one meaning (such as with "protection.")

- *Identification.* What is the identification of the record? Is it a title, an attachment letter, a form identification, or a document number? The documented procedure or matrix will indicate the unique identification for each record within the system.

■ *Storage*. Where is each record being maintained? This is typically as specific as stating a particular function or office of the facility.

■ *Protection*. How is each record being protected? Typical protections include storing records in fireproof containers, limiting access to them, or backing up electronic records storage.

■ *Retrieval*. How can each record be retrieved? This can also be called indexing. Examples of how records may be retrieved include customer number, date, shift, product number, employee last name, and region of the world.

■ *Retention time*. This is how long you intend to maintain each record. As with the other control variables, it's possible that every single record may have a different retention time. It's worth noting that ISO 9001 provides no guidance on the appropriate retention times of records. This is completely up to the organization and its needs. I have seen retention times from one week to twenty years.

■ *Disposition*. This refers to what happens to the record after the retention time has elapsed. Typical dispositions include archive, shred, or recycle.

Legible, identifiable, and retrievable

ISO 9001 requires that records be legible, which means they are in a condition and language that enables them to be understood. Records that are burned, spindled, mutilated, or otherwise unreadable would not be considered legible. Legibility could also mean that they are readable in the language primarily used by the organization.

Records must also be readily identifiable. This means that they are titled, numbered, or otherwise identified in a clear manner, and that they are traceable to the process or activity that produced them. They must also be retrievable when needed.

"Retrievable" means that the records can be located and retrieved within a reasonable amount of time. Of course, this is quite subjective. Records stored on-site are typically retrievable within a day at the most. Records stored off-site may take longer. If your organization has unusual limitations or requirements related to retrievability, then you will want to describe these clearly in your records procedure.

The strategic importance of records

I often describe record keeping as a simple housekeeping function. That's basically what it is, but it's important to remember that records can have strategic im-

Figure 2.3   Sample Records Matrix

Type of record	Identification	Storage	Protection	Retrieval	Retention Time	Disposition
Calibration records	Form 306, or titled "Certificate of calibration" or similar	Technician's file cabinets	Accessible by technician & ops manager	Filed by equipment number	Life of the gage	Recycled
Training records	Form 201	HR office	Accessible by HR manager	Filed by employee last name	Term of employment, plus one year	Recycled
Inspection records	Forms 405, 555, 543	Ops manager office	Accessible by ops manager & shift supervisors	Filed by date	One year	Archive for three additional years
Nonconforming materials records	Form 320	Supervisor's file cabinets	Accessible by ops manager & shift supervisors	Filed by date	Six months	Recycled
Management Review minutes & attachments	Titled "Management Review Minutes" or similar	V.P.'s file cabinet	Accessible by V.P. & management rep	Filed by date	Three years	Recycled
Purchase orders	ACME purchase order	Purchasing database	Accessible by purchasing personnel	By date or purchase order number	Three years	Recycled
Corrective & preventive actions	ACME CA/PA	Corrective action database	Accessible by quality manager	By date or CA/PA#	Three years	Recycled
Internal audit records	Various identifiers	Internal audit database	Accessible by quality manager	By date or audit#	Three years	Recycled
Etc.						

portance. Records facilitate problem solving by providing traceability for products and processes. If we have a customer complaint, records enable us to determine when the product was created, what resources were used, what personnel were involved, and what specifications and controls were in place at the time. We now have a factual basis for problem solving. Without these records, all we have is guesswork.

For organizations that produce sensitive, regulated, or potentially dangerous products, control of records is a matter of survival. Failing to maintain records in a systematic manner can lead to people going to jail and cessation of operations. Examples of these products include the following:

- Medical devices
- Drugs
- Nuclear power
- Aircrafts
- Aircraft parts
- Firearms and explosives
- Food and beverages

FREQUENTLY ASKED QUESTIONS

Can we specify two weeks as the retention time for a particular record?

If two weeks is as long as you need to retain a record, then that's your decision. ISO 9001 does not provide any guidance on retention times.

Is it OK to combine our procedures for record control into our document control procedure?

You can combine the procedures if you want. However, it could cause some confusion since documents are fundamentally different than records.

Chapter 3

ISO 9001 Section 5 Management Responsibility

Management's responsibility for quality and the effective functioning of the organization is addressed in section 5 of ISO 9001. This is notable because the first three words of every clause are "Top management shall…" This leaves no confusion about who is accountable for these requirements: top management.

Who exactly is top management? It's the person or people who lead the organization at its highest levels. The role of top management cannot be delegated to people who don't lead the organization. It's categorically impossible for top management to play a passive role in the management system. Top managers will be involved in a very active manner, and the management system will become one of their keys tools for planning, execution, and improvement.

Make sure to specify exactly who is considered to be top management within the scope of your system. Top management can be more than one person, but if you choose to do this, then all the people considered to be top management will have to fulfill the requirements of section 5.

5.1 MANAGEMENT COMMITMENT

The essence of clause 5.1, Management commitment, is that top management must *actively* demonstrate its commitment to the management system. Abstract commitment is not enough. Most of the commitments required in clause 5.1 are addressed elsewhere within ISO 9001.

Communicating the importance of meeting requirements

Top management must communicate the importance of meeting customer, statutory, and regulatory requirements. This communication falls into two general categories: customer requirements, and statutory and regulatory requirements. It's quite common for top management to communicate customer requirements of various sorts. Topics could include:

- Changes in customer requirements
- Emerging customer expectations
- Customer service successes
- Customer complaints
- Best practices from inside or outside the organization
- Feedback trends
- Product innovations to address customer needs
- Procedural guidelines
- Actions of competitors relating to customers
- The needs of internal customers

The category of "communicating the importance of the customer" is very broad and can encompass almost anything. The intent is to ensure that top management takes a leadership role in driving customer understanding. The message is expected to come directly from top management; it should never be delivered by someone else. In large organizations, the customer sometimes becomes invisible. People begin to forget why the organization exists. Top management has to remind everyone of the organization's core purpose (meeting the needs of its customers) and communicate this message often enough that it becomes part of the organization's culture.

The second type of communication relates to statutory and regulatory requirements facing the organization. The exact topics and magnitude of communication will depend on the nature of the organization. Here are some examples of this type of communication:

- Product safety
- Workplace safety
- Environmental regulatory compliance
- Product labeling
- Transportation safety
- The maintenance of a harassment-free workplace
- Equal-opportunity employment

This communication can be done via e-mail, memo, video, in person, or in a variety of other ways. ISO 9001 does not explicitly require that there be records of top management's communication; however, records could certainly build the case for the communication it requires.

Establishing the quality policy

The quality policy is the organization's general commitment to quality and other principles in which it believes. Top management must demonstrate how it has led the development of the quality policy. This can be achieved by discussing how managers influenced the development of the policy. Top management's formal approval of the policy will indicate its commitment. The quality policy is covered in more detail in clause 5.3.

Ensuring the establishment of objectives

Quality objectives are the measurable goals embraced by the organization. Top management will either determine objectives or ensure that others determine them. Proof of managers' commitment to objectives could be achieved by any of the following actions, among others:

■ Discussing why each of the objectives are important
■ Providing examples of how the organization is working toward objectives
■ Indicating how management led or influenced the determination of objectives
■ Providing evidence of progress toward objectives
■ Approving the objectives through managers' signatures or other means

Quality objectives shouldn't be established simply to meet the requirements of ISO 9001. They should make the organization more competitive, and that certainly is something top management needs to be intimately involved in. Objectives are discussed in more detail in subclause 5.4.1.

Conducting management reviews

Management review is the process for top management to review the performance of the management system and the organization as a whole. It's one of the most important processes in the entire system. Note that this requirement dictates that top management will "conduct management reviews." In other words, top managers must play an active role and provide leadership for this activity. Management review is not intended to be something done just to satisfy ISO 9001 requirements; rather, it's top management's opportunity to analyze data, make decisions, and take actions. Management review is discussed in more detail in clause 5.6.

Ensuring the availability of resources

Resources enable everything that the organization does. Unless top management commits resources, they generally don't become available. Top management must ensure that the organization has the capital, equipment, tools, personnel, and other resources to be effective and to drive customer satisfaction. This can be demonstrated through budgets, strategies, meeting minutes, or other planning tools.

FREQUENTLY ASKED QUESTIONS

Do we have to keep records of top management communicating about the importance of customer, statutory, and regulatory requirements?

ISO 9001 does not require records here. If there's a different way of verifying that the communication took place, that would suffice as evidence. In the absence of records, ask a variety of personnel if the communication took place and what was addressed.

Top management of our organization is the vice president of operations, but she has designated that the plant manager act as top management for ISO 9001 purposes. Is this OK?

No. Top management is whoever leads your organization at its highest levels. This can't be delegated downward.

5.2 CUSTOMER FOCUS

Clause 5.2 includes one of the shortest requirements in the entire standard. It's a single sentence, very general in nature: "Top management shall ensure that customer requirements are determined and are met with the aim of enhancing customer satisfaction." This requirement is typically achieved by performing actions that are required in other sections of ISO 9001. The main point of the section is to emphasize the fact that top management is essential to determining and meeting customer requirements, and to enhancing customer satisfaction. The issues that top management cares about are the issues other people will care about, too. Leadership's customer focus is contagious.

Determining and meeting customer requirements

In very small organizations, top management is personally involved in determining and meeting customer requirements. For most organizations, however, top management empowers others to determine and meet customer requirements. As long as top management has ensured that this happens, the spirit of the requirement has been met. Top management achieves this primarily through ensuring resources are provided for the following activities:

■ Staffing positions that determine customer requirements

■ Clearly defining responsibilities and authorities

■ Training personnel in customer communications

■ Developing procedures for taking orders and for product realization

This requirement is closely related to subclauses 7.2.1, Determination of requirements related to the product, and 7.2.2, Review of requirements related to the product. If top management has empowered and resourced these processes, it has generally addressed this requirement.

This section of the standard also emphasizes top management's responsibility to enhance customer satisfaction. Although top managers may not personally enhance customer satisfaction, they will certainly be involved to some degree. Here are some of the ways that top management can enhance customer satisfaction:

■ Ensure that customer feedback is collected.

■ Analyze that feedback.

■ Determine improvements based on the most significant feedback.

■ Monitor progress on improvements.

■ Communicate customer feedback trends.

This requirement is closely related to subclause 8.2.1, Customer satisfaction, and clause 5.6, Management review. Top management will be more actively involved in enhancing customer satisfaction because it's an explicit input to management review. In the most effective organizations, top management is well aware of trends in customer feedback and the actions taken to address it. Managers' awareness and interest shines a spotlight on customer satisfaction, prioritizing it to the entire organization.

FREQUENTLY ASKED QUESTIONS

Do I need to do anything specific in this section? It seems like we would satisfy 5.2 by implementing other parts of the ISO 9001 standard.

You don't need to do anything specific unless you see the need to do so. This section of ISO 9001 is often met through achievement of other requirements.

We would like to introduce the concept of "internal customers" to our employees. Can we do this as part of ISO 9001?

Yes, of course. The concept of internal customers is very powerful, though it's not specifically addressed by ISO 9001.

5.3 QUALITY POLICY

The quality policy is top management's overall direction and philosophy related to quality. It's typically a short document, often less than 100 words. The policy is often structured as a series of bulleted commitments, though you could adapt whatever format is appropriate. The quality policy communicates to everyone in the organization what is truly important to the organization's success. You aren't obligated to call your quality policy by that name. It could just as well be called a mission statement, vision, charter, statement of excellence, or any number of other names. In fact, there are good reasons for not using the word "quality" as part of its name, since quality has a very narrowly defined meaning in some organizations. Your policy must address the following points:

■ *Be appropriate to the purpose of the organization.* This means that the quality policy relates to the core purpose and activities of the organization. In fact, it may briefly describe what the organization does. Keep in mind that most quality policies are fewer than 100 words, so this description will be very brief. If there are special concerns of the organization (such as safety for an organization that manufactures dynamite, or confidentiality for an organization that performs mental health services), then these concerns may also be addressed in the policy. A generic quality policy wouldn't satisfy these special requirements. If your quality policy could be adopted by ACME Widget Co. without any changes, you need to rewrite it.

■ *Include a commitment to meeting requirements and continual improvement.* This means exactly what it says. The organization must commit to meeting requirements and continual improvement. The easiest and most obvious way to do this is to use these exact words in your policy, although you could certainly paraphrase the commitment or put your own spin on it.

■ *Provide a framework for establishing and reviewing objectives.* The quality policy, either directly or indirectly, must provide a structure for using objectives. This can be satisfied by including language that says something like, "We are committed to establishing and reviewing objectives as part of our continual improvement effort," or it could be satisfied by the implication of measurable objectives. However, don't include your specific objectives within your quality policy. Objectives are subject to change on a regular basis, and the policy is more of a thematic document that will change less frequently.

■ *Communicated and understood within the organization.* The policy is a key document. As such, it will be communicated broadly and frequently. The policy must also be understood. Keep in mind that employees don't need to memorize the quality policy to understand it. Personnel typically understand some of the key points of the policy to apply them to their positions. The education campaign on the quality policy will most likely be one of the earliest training efforts within the implementation of the management system.

■ *Reviewed for continuing suitability.* Nothing lasts forever, not even a quality policy. Despite its appropriateness, the passage of time can render it obsolete. In my experience, this is often between four and six years of being drafted. ISO 9001 requires that the policy be regularly reviewed for continuing suitability. The general interpretation is that top management should review the quality policy at least once a year, although organizations could certainly review it more often if they felt the need. The management review function (see 5.6) is the most common forum for reviewing the quality policy.

| **Figure 3.1** | **Sample Quality Policy** |

ACME Inc. Quality Policy

ACME Inc. is committed to providing precision machine parts for aerospace and defense applications. In pursuit of this, we are dedicated to the following points:

■ Meet or exceed our customers' expectations and all other relevant requirements

■ Achieve continual improvement of our operations and performance

■ Establish objectives to help communicate organizational direction and drive improvements

---

President

FREQUENTLY ASKED QUESTIONS

Do we need to actually say in our quality policy that it will be communicated and understood?

Not unless you want to. Those are requirements related to implementing the policy, not commitments, that must be stated within the policy.

Does the quality policy have to be signed by top management?

No. There must be some evidence of top management's approval, but this could be demonstrated through meeting minutes, approval of the quality manual, or other means.

What's the difference between our quality policy and quality objectives?

The quality policy is a set of general commitments, while the quality objectives are specific metrics or goals. They are linked together thematically, but are generally different documents.

5.4 PLANNING

5.4.1 Quality objectives

Quality objectives are measurable goals that relate to your organization's commitments to quality. Quality is a very broad topic, however. ISO 9000 defines quality as the degree to which an inherent set of characteristics meets requirements. This opens up the world of quality objectives to just about any characteristic that matters to the organization's success. As a result, objectives can address a wide range of topics: product conformance, process performance, customer satisfaction, workplace safety, financial results, market share, cost reduction, and many others. When reviewing objectives that aren't traditional quality measures, I have heard auditors utter the comment, "These quality objectives aren't sufficiently related to quality." This is ridiculous. As long as quality objectives measure the degree to which characteristics conform to requirements, they are fine.

There is a good argument for not even using the term "quality objectives." The term can mislead personnel into thinking that these metrics can only address topics related to quality control or quality assurance. As we've already discussed, quality objectives can relate to almost anything that bears on the organization's success. If a different name reinforces that point, then by all means substitute the term quality objectives with a different name. Good alternatives include *business objectives*, *scorecard goals*, *key measures*, and *performance targets*. There is nothing in ISO 9001 that says you must use the same terminology as the standard. If you decide to re-name your quality objectives, it would be helpful to note this in your quality manual.

Top management shall ensure quality objectives

This sentence reiterates the requirement from subclause 5.1c, which includes top management's need to take a leadership role in defining quality objectives. Managers must select the objectives or tell appropriate employees how to select them. Either way, top management should be involved in the determination of objectives early in the process. Make sure that top management understands that these objectives are being established to become more successful, not just for meeting ISO 9001 requirements.

Objectives to meet requirements for product

At least one of your quality objectives must be related to your product. Obvious candidates include:

- Inspection results
- Product reliability
- Service effectiveness
- On-time delivery performance
- Warranty returns
- Jobs completed according to plan
- Services requiring rework

Keep customer needs and feedback in mind when setting project objectives. Whether your product is a good or a service, you must establish an objective that's related to the product's conformance.

Established at relevant functions and levels

What exactly does it mean when ISO 9001 says that quality objectives must be established at relevant functions and levels? I'll clear it up for you very quickly. Everyone who's irrelevant raise your hand. What, no hands? Does that mean that everyone plays a role in providing the organization's products, at least at some level? The answer is yes. All organizations are composed of a supply chain of internal functions, all working together. Any break in that supply chain affects the organization's ability to provide its products. Thus, all functions and levels are relevant.

That said, everyone within the scope of the management system will have quality objectives. These will either be organizationwide objectives that apply to everyone or functional objectives that specifically address departmental responsibilities and output. Objectives can even be a mix of both. However, no one can plausibly claim that no objectives are applicable to them. Your quality objectives will touch everybody in the organization in some manner, and everybody will have the ability to contribute to their achievement.

Objectives shall be measurable

This point is very simple, but it bears explanation. An organization's quality objectives must be measurable and they must define exactly how the desired state will be achieved. General themes, philosophies, and aspirations rarely constitute measurable objectives. Although ISO 9001's guidelines are quite straightforward, vague objectives abound, such as:

- *Incorporate excellence into all we do.*

- *Offer a challenging and rewarding environment for our employees.*
- *Earn the respect of our neighbors in the community.*
- *Create an unmatched service experience for all our customers.*
- *Make associates proud they joined our team.*

Despite being admirable concepts, these aren't measurable objectives. However, they could serve as possible first steps toward measurable objectives. The trick is to look at lofty aspirations and ask, "What indicates whether we've done that or not?" Keep asking that question until you uncover a metric that gets to the heart of success or failure. Get specific about what you're trying to achieve. Platitudes such as *incorporate excellence into all we do* are so vague they serve no purpose.

The main reason for setting measurable objectives has nothing to do with ISO 9001 and everything to do with becoming more successful. People have trouble contributing to fuzzy, undefined objectives. They can't tell whether their efforts are making a difference because the objective can't be gauged. As a consequence, the organization begins to drift like a rudderless boat. However, measurable objectives focus everyone's energies and creative powers. Combined with leadership and an empowered work force, measurable objectives pave the way to success.

Objectives shall be consistent with the quality policy

Quality objectives must be aligned with the themes of the quality policy. This means that any special claims or commitments the organization included in its quality policy must be backed up by objectives. You can't just make a statement in the quality policy and expect the words to magically transform the organization; you've got to develop an objective that will illustrate your success or failure. Carefully examine your quality policy and make sure that anything above and beyond the minimum commitments required by ISO 9001 is supported by an objective.

Years ago I worked for a company that put this statement into its quality policy: *We are committed to long-term partnerships with our customer and suppliers.* An auditor rightfully asked the question, "Do you have any objectives relating to long-term partnerships?" Of course we didn't. Nobody had interpreted the requirement literally, which is exactly the way it should be interpreted.

Objectives shall be documented. This requirement is actually in subclause 4.2.1, but I repeat it here as a reminder. Document your objectives and include all relevant details related to them, including:

- Where data on the objectives comes from

Figure 5.2   **Sample Quality Objectives—ACME Inc.**

Document No: ACME-002   *Revision date:* 3-11-08   *Page 1 of 1*

ACME Inc. Quality Objectives

1. **Efficiency.** Calculated by dividing the total number of scrapped and re-worked items by the total number of items produced (both good and bad).

$$1 - [(\text{total scrapped} + \text{reworked parts} + \text{downgraded parts}) / \text{total parts produced}] = \text{efficiency}$$

Efficiency target = 97.5% or better

2. **On-time delivery.** Calculated by dividing the total number of products that were delivered on or before their promise date by the total number of goods in the same period.

On-time deliveries / all deliveries = on-time delivery percentage

On-time delivery target = 98% or better

3. **Net income.** Calculated by subtracting all expenses from the total revenue on a monthly basis. Expenses include cash expenses, payables, credits, interest payments, depreciation, and taxes. Revenues include cash collections and receivables.

Revenues − (expenses + interest payments + depreciation + taxes) = profit

Profit target = $800,000/month

4. **Customer loyalty index.** Calculated by determining the percentage of customers who "strongly agree" that they will recommend our company to a colleague.

Customer loyalty index target = 86%

Approved by:_____ Date:_____

- How often data on the objectives should be collected
- Who collects the data
- Any necessary calculations
- Reporting and communication requirements

These items are not explicitly required by ISO 9001, but they are generally necessary to manage objectives. The resulting objectives can often be documented in a page or two. Regardless of the format or length, it must be treated like any other document and include approvals, revision status, and other controls described in subclause 4.2.3, Control of documents.

FREQUENTLY ASKED QUESTIONS

Everyone in our organization has his or her own personal objectives. Does this satisfy ISO 9001 requirements?

Maybe. The intent of this requirement is to determine organizational objectives, not personal objectives. Make sure that you have established objectives on a broader scale (organizational, functional, or departmental). Personal objectives may then stem from the higher-level objectives, if that's the way your organization wants to operate.

Can we include our quality objectives in our quality policy?

You can if you want, but it makes more sense to maintain them as separate documents. The objectives are likely to change much more often than the policy.

Can we use "profit" as a quality objective? Our consultant told us we can't because it has nothing to do with quality.

Yes, you can use profit as a quality objective. Quality is a very broad topic and can encompass nearly anything the organization does. Profit certainly reflects on the quality of your processes and products.

5.4.2 Quality management system planning

Quality management system planning requires organizations to plot the various components of their systems: the processes, procedures, checks, and other controls that ensure that work is carried out effectively. Most organizations plan their QMSs when they are first implemented. The organization must also maintain and evolve its system as circumstances change. In life, few things are static, and a management system is likely to change and improve on a regular basis. Document control is closely aligned with this requirement, as it is how changes are formally made to most processes.

Planning must meet requirements in 4.1

This makes reference to clause 4.1 as a starting point for planning. To some degree that makes sense. Clause 4.1 asks the organization to describe the sequence and interaction of its processes, and doing this can reveal a lot about what planning will be needed in establishing a management system. Start with the high-level diagram of your organization and build the more detailed processes around it.

Planning must meet requirements of quality objectives

This provides another starting point for planning your organization's objectives. And guess what? It makes a lot of sense. Determine your organization's objectives, and then build controls, procedures, records, checks, training, and other processes around meeting those objectives. Taken literally, determining objectives would be one of the very first steps of implementing a management system. That's not the way most organizations do it, but it would result in a much more relevant and strategic system.

Maintain integrity of the management system during changes

This requirement reminds you that your system must evolve to meet the changing demands of the marketplace. Many changes have the potential to trigger revisions and enhancements to your management system, such as:

■ New products
■ New customers
■ New equipment and processes
■ New personnel
■ New competitors

How will you know when circumstances change in your organization? Your internal audit process will tell you. Management review will also consider changes long before they happen, providing an opportunity for the management system to evolve.

5.5.1 Responsibility and authority

ISO 9001 requires that the organization define the responsibilities and authorities of all personnel. Responsibility is what personnel must *do*, and authority is what they are *empowered* to do. It's worth noting that this requirement uses the word "define," which usually means that the requirements be documented to define them consistently. Only the smallest organizations could effectively communicate responsibilities and authorities without some sort of documentation. Responsibility and authority can be defined in procedures, job descriptions, or a variety of other places. Once responsibility and authority are defined, they must be communicated to personnel. Simply making the documentation available to personnel would be one way of communicating responsibilities and authorities. Incorporating it into training would be another way.

Job descriptions are an especially widespread way of meeting this requirement. If your human resources department already has job descriptions on file, it could be a simple matter of making sure they are current. You will also need to apply document control to them, since they are within the scope of the management system.

FREQUENTLY ASKED QUESTION

Can we use an organizational chart to define responsibility and authority?
Probably not. An organizational chart usually shows reporting relationships and organizational structure, not responsibilities and authorities.

5.5.2 Management representative

The management representative is the champion of the management system. This person doesn't own the system, but he or she takes the lead in making sure it is established, implemented, and maintained. The role of management representative is especially important, because it influences many of the decisions about the design and function of the management system. An effective management representative is usually someone who is energetic, persistent, and diplomatic. He or she must not be afraid to light a fire under people who fail to contribute.

Top management shall appoint a member of the organization's management

There must be proof that top management appointed the management representative. The appointment is another indication of top management's active involvement in the management system. The evidence of the appointment could come from a memo, e-mail, meeting records, or a statement within the quality manual, among other sources.

The management representation must be a member of the organization's management

This usually means that the management representative must be an employee of the organization. It's possible for a consultant to be a member of management, and thus the management representative, but it's much more effective if this role is carried out by an employee of the organization. Regardless of who assumes the role, the management representative must have the ability to make management decisions and apply resources. The management representative often reports directly to top management, though this is not a requirement.

Management representative shall ensure system processes

The management representative will ensure that the QMS processes are established, implemented, and maintained. This is the project management aspect of being a management representative. Establishing, implementing, and maintaining a QMS requires the management representative to coordinate many different efforts and continually sell the benefits of the system. However, it bears repeating that the management representative does not own the system. Everybody owns the management system, but top management leads the effort to maintain and champion it.

Report to top management on effectiveness

The management representative will report to top management on the effectiveness of the management system. This happens during management review, a very important process that is addressed in clause 5.6. The management representative doesn't need to personally collect and present the data on effectiveness, but he or she makes sure it happens. The most effective management reviews involve a wide range of organizational managers and influencers, with the management representative coordinating their input.

Ensure the promotion of awareness of customer requirements

This basically means that the management representative must help promote a customer focus throughout the organization. There is nothing more important to the organization's success than the customer, and the management representative must continually remind everyone of this fact. Customer awareness can be accomplished in many ways, but here are a few simple methods:

- Posting data on customer feedback trends
- Publishing product specifications
- Holding meetings that address customer issues
- Serving as a liaison between the organization and the customer
- Distributing memos and e-mails that clarify customer requirements

Who makes a good management representative?

It's not uncommon for management system efforts to fail for no other reason than the management representative did not have the ability to drive the effort forward. For this reason, a number of important attributes should be considered when selecting a management representative:

- *Enthusiasm.* It's hard for people to be naturally excited about a management system. However, it's the management representative's responsibility to create excitement about the system by being enthusiastic about what it can do for the future success of the organization and its employees.
- *Motivation.* Because the management representative often works independently, he or she must be completely self-motivated and able to work without supervision. When the management representative needs assistance, he or she must be mature enough to seek it.
- *Organization.* Everyone has a different organization system, but the important thing is that such a system exists. The management representative must be able to organize multiple tasks and contingencies, always knowing each task's progress. This is not a job for someone who is easily overwhelmed by complexity.
- *Respect.* The management representative must be someone that everyone within the organization respects. This will enable the representative to command authority and motivate employees.
- *Diplomacy.* The management representative must realize that everyone has feelings. He or she will motivate colleagues and spur action with tact and diplomacy.

FREQUENTLY ASKED QUESTION

Since we're very small, can we just have a consultant act as our management representative?

Technically, yes, as long as the consultant is considered a member of management. However, you should strive to have this role performed by an actual employee. It's a great learning opportunity and an employee will always feel more commitment than a consultant.

5.5.3 Internal communication

Internal communication is the oil that flows through the gears of the organization. Most organizations have plenty of communications: meetings, e-mail, telephone, teleconferences, newsletters, and bulletin boards. The trick is to use these opportunities to communicate about the organization's management system. Typical topics of communication include audit results, customer feedback, corrective actions, management review actions and decisions, progress toward objectives, and many others. The organization must deliberately plan communication and then have the discipline to carry it out. Top management is integral in ensuring the proper communication happens.

FREQUENTLY ASKED QUESTION

Do we need to develop a communication procedure?

Not unless you think you need one.

5.6 Management review

Management review is one of the most important components of the management system. It is the process by which top management reviews the effectiveness of the system and analyzes the performance of the organization. ISO 9001 does not include any guidance for how often this process should take place, but common sense dictates that it should happen regularly. Smart organizations align their management reviews with the regular cycle of reviewing organizational performance, which usually takes place on a monthly basis. However, the frequency is up to the organization.

Adding a meeting called *ISO 9001 management review* when there is already an existing performance review of the organization is nearly always a bad idea. For starters, no one needs another meeting to attend. Second, if it comes down to a choice between ISO 9001 management review and the existing performance meeting, which one is going to prevail? The existing meeting will win, of course. Incorporate your management review into any existing performance review forums. You may have to add a topic or two to the agenda, but this is a much better option than establishing a completely new meeting for the purpose of meeting ISO 9001 requirements.

It's also worth noting that nothing in ISO 9001 says that management review will be a physical meeting. ISO 9001 requires that top management and the management representative take part, but beyond these two participants, it's up to the organization to decide who else to involve. Typically, organizations include their key decision makers as part of management review. No matter how the organization configures its management review, it must produce records.

The ultimate purpose of management review is to help the organization to improve. Management review does this by analyzing information, making decisions, and taking the appropriate actions. It's not a passive process. If management review does not produce actions or decisions, it's failing in its duty to drive improvements.

Management review inputs

ISO 9001 requires specific inputs to management review. The inputs are data and information that reveal organizational and management system effectiveness. These inputs include:

- *Audit results.* This information could include positives, nonconformities, and improvement opportunities. As with all information presented to top management, strive for a concise message. Use charts and graphics whenever possible. If there have been no audits since the last management review, mention this in the records.

- *Customer feedback.* Customer feedback is the most important communication the organization can receive, and top management must analyze and interpret it. Focus on the trends that deserve attention and take action on the big issues. Keep in mind that customer feedback can be simultaneously proactive and reactive, positive and negative.

- *Process performance and product conformity.* How are our processes running and what indicates that our products meet requirements? This is really two different inputs rolled into one. Process performance can be reflected by audit results, which illustrates that some of these required inputs can be satisfied by the same evidence. Examples of product conformity include inspection results, field failures, service success rate, errors discovered, and products requiring rework.

■ *Status of corrective and preventive actions.* Corrective action is the formal process for solving problems, and preventive action is the process for preventing problems before they occur. Both of these are critically important and deserve top management's careful scrutiny. Typical information presented during management review includes how many actions have been opened, how many actions have been closed, and the categories of corrective and preventive actions. Because top management has the power to motivate action from people, other good topics to consider are overdue actions and those that aren't making progress.

■ *Follow-up actions from previous management reviews.* Anyone who has ever attended a meeting knows that it can be difficult to know what was decided. Even when it *is* clear, it's almost always difficult to complete the agreed-upon action items. This input ties the management reviews together and ensures that action items don't get forgotten.

■ *Changes that could affect the QMS.* These could include changes related to economics, demographics, competition, suppliers, products, processes, laws, or anything else that affects the organization. It's helpful to keep a running file of newspaper and magazine articles related to issues affecting your company. These can be consolidated into concise packets of information that are presented during management review.

■ *Improvement recommendations.* Improvement is the point of management review, and some of the key inputs will be ideas and recommendations from various parts of the organization. An employee suggestion system can yield great improvement ideas. Recommendations for improvement can also be developed by the management representative or other managers prior to the meeting, and then proposed to top management during management review.

The standard's intent is that the organization addresses all required inputs within the cycle defined by its management review. If the organization commits to a monthly management review, then records would indicate that all inputs were reviewed within that month-long time frame. An effective format for management review records can be a matrix that shows the input topics in the left-hand column, and the actual data discussed in the right-hand column. Because there are so many inputs that must be accounted for, make record keeping as systematic and error-proof as possible.

Management review outputs

ISO 9001 requires that management review produce specific outputs. These outputs are actions or decisions related to three items:

■ *Improvement of processes and the management system.* Based on the data presented, is there anything you need to change about your management system or your processes? Do you need any new procedures or controls? Is a new training program needed in part of your organization? Is communication effective? Keep in mind that sometimes removing or streamlining a procedure is what may be needed. Continually adding to the bulk and magnitude of the management system is rarely a good idea.

■ *Product improvement.* Based on what you discussed, do any products need to be improved? Are new features needed? Should different verifications be applied to the product? Should entirely new products and services be designed? Customer feedback is an especially good input for understanding what should be improved about your product.

■ *Resource needs.* Nothing happens without resources. Because you have top management in attendance, management review is the perfect place to secure resources. Supplemented by good data and convincing messages, it should be relatively easy to secure the resources needed to drive improvement.

Just as the inputs to management review must be recorded, so must the outputs. Actions that come from management review are often recorded as preventive actions and tracked through that system. No matter how they are handled, make sure they become inputs to the next management review.

FREQUENTLY ASKED QUESTIONS

Our general manager is frequently out of town and it's very difficult to schedule management review. Can he delegate someone to attend management review on his behalf?

No. Your management review process must involve top management. Perhaps you could explore creative ways of involving the general manager in management review when he is out of town.

Does management review have to be an actual meeting, or can we have a virtual meeting via teleconference or webinar?

Management review does not have to be an actual meeting. As long as you cover the required inputs and outputs, you can conduct management review in any way you see fit.

We would like to address different inputs of management review in different meetings. For instance, process performance and product conformity is something we talk about in our weekly staff meeting. Customer feedback gets addressed at our monthly roundtable. Will this approach meet ISO 9001 requirements?

Yes. You can structure your management review in any way that makes sense to you, as long as it involves top management and the management representative, at a minimum.

We're performing management review once a year. What's your opinion of this?

Although this may satisfy minimum requirements, it doesn't sound very proactive or effective. I would strongy consider performing it more often.

Chapter 4

ISO 9001 Section 6 Resource Management

Section 6 of ISO 9001 is composed of four relatively brief clauses. As its title indicates, this section addresses how the organization acquires and manages its resources.

6.1 PROVISION OF RESOURCES

ISO 9001 requires that the organization determine the resources it needs to be successful. Specifically, this includes resources needed for the management system to function and for the achievement of customer satisfaction. Let's take a brief look at both of these.

Resources for the management system

Resources for the management system can be determined in a variety of ways, but the most obvious opportunity is during management review. In fact, one of the formal outputs of management review is its review of resource needs. If this management review output is satisfied, you have also satisfied the resources requirement of subclause 6.1a.

Resources to enhance customer satisfaction

This category of resources can be addressed through the outputs of management review. It can also be covered during strategic planning, staff meetings, marketing meetings, and budgetary sessions.

6.2 HUMAN RESOURCES

ISO 9001's training requirements are located in clause 6.2. ISO 9001 states that all training must be based on competency needs. It defines competency as a mix of education, training, skills, and experience. Different roles in the organization have different competency requirements, and the trick is to determine what is needed for the employee to perform effectively.

6.2.1 General
Personnel performing work affecting conformity to product requirements

This section starts by defining exactly which employees must be addressed in the organization's training process. At first glance, its focus seems quite narrow: Personnel who work on the product. However, if you take a supply chain view of the organization, you begin to understand that everyone's work affects product conformity at some level. The training process must include the full range of personnel performing work affecting product conformity, including:

- Top management
- Salaried personnel
- Hourly personnel
- Supervisors and managers
- Temporary employees
- Research and technical personnel
- Recent hires

Many employees can be grouped together based on common roles and job functions; two employees with different job titles won't necessarily have different competency requirements. The converse is also true: Personnel working in the same area and doing ostensibly the same job may actually have differing competency requirements. The bottom line is that organizations need to eliminate their outdated paradigms regarding the way work is performed and who performs it. It's helpful to think about the organization as a series of processes rather than as a collection of departments. The determination of competency requirements is an eye-opening exercise when performed in a thoughtful manner.

Competent on the basis of appropriate education, training, skills, and experience

This requirement mandates that everyone who affects product conformity (i.e., everyone in the organization) must be competent. So, what exactly is "competent?" It's the condition that enables a person to perform a task in a manner that meets the required performance standard. ISO 9001 clarifies the issue by establishing that competence is the practical application of four variables:

■ *Education.* The formal knowledge-building that takes place over an extended time frame, typically delivered through a school of some sort. The traditional method of delivering education is through classroom instruction, although virtual methods of education have become very popular in recent years.

■ *Training.* Concentrated learning that focuses on a practical application. Most formal educational programs require months or years to complete, but training can often be completed in a matter of hours. The goal of training is usually to equip the student with the ability to perform a very specific set of tasks.

■ *Skills.* The abilities that personnel are able to apply, and are developed through training or experience. In this way, skills are usually the products of effective training or experience. Some skills are required by personnel before they are even considered for a position, while other skills are developed over time.

■ *Experience.* The direct participation in an activity, job, or role. Whereas training and education can be somewhat abstract, experience is concrete. Some jobs require a significant amount of experience because training and education don't provide full exposure to the necessary abilities.

The mix of these four variables—education, training, skills, and experience—will differ depending on the type of job being analyzed. A college professor's competency needs are overwhelmingly concentrated around education and training, with relatively less emphasis on tangible skills and experience. A glass blower, on the other hand, probably requires a great many more skills developed through experience. Just as the college professor and glass blower have drastically different competency needs, most employees' competencies span a wide range, depending on the activities being performed.

6.2.2 Competence, training, and awareness
Determine necessary competence

This repeats the requirement above in slightly different terms. The organization must decide what specific competencies are necessary for someone to perform effectively. As we discussed, competency requirements can be developed for individual jobs or groupings of similar jobs; it all depends on the organization's needs. I have seen simple organizations that had four sets of competencies that addressed everyone and more complex organizations that had hundreds of different competency standards.

To be fully effective and useful, competency requirements must meet the following requirements. These are not specific ISO 9001 requirements, but they are practical matters that should at least be considered.

■ *Realistic.* Competency requirements must reflect the needs of the activity being performed. Venerable job descriptions, although dog-eared and handed down through the years, may not provide much guidance. Observe the jobs being performed and then talk to the people performing the jobs and to their supervisors. If practical, get input from the customer (internal or external) who receives the job's output. Be careful not to overstate competency needs; make sure that a job really requires a college degree and two years of experience before designating these as competency needs.

■ *Demonstrable.* The person performing the activity must be able to demonstrate his or her competencies, particularly as they relate to skills. This means that the organization must be specific and descriptive when defining competency. *Excellent communication skills* is very vague. Take this statement and deconstruct it into its demonstrable elements: *Ability to prepare written reports using computer word processing programs; ability to prepare and deliver formal presentations to top management using audiovisual tools.* With clearly demonstrable competency needs established, it's much easier to identify gaps.

■ *Forward-looking.* The organization should consider its future needs—as far as they can be predicted—as well as present needs. This is where training and strategy begin to intersect. Of course, if strategy hasn't been communicated throughout the organization, this intersection will not be possible. Keep in mind that the forward-looking view of competence must still be based in reality. Competency needs probably can't be projected more than a year into the future and still remain realistic.

■ *Documented.* ISO 9001 doesn't specifically require that competency needs be documented, but it does say that they must be determined. As we discussed earlier, *determine* is one of those words that comes very close to *document.* Without documentation of some sort, how will the organization ensure consistent application and communication of competencies? Document control would most certainly apply to documented competency needs.

Provide training or take other actions to achieve competence

Once competency requirements have been determined for all personnel affecting product conformity, the organization must compare individuals to its competency needs and identify where gaps exist, then provide appropriate training, if needed. This approach can result in significant cost savings because it eliminates unnecessary training. It also sends a valuable signal to employees that management understands the needs of a given job or function and is willing to ensure that employees possess the requisite education, training, skills, and experience to succeed in their roles.

A wide range of actions can satisfy gaps in competency, and the action taken may actually be a combination of individual actions to constitute training. Examples include:

- On-the-job training
- Classroom training
- Independent study (traditional, audio, video, and Internet-based)
- Degree and certificate programs through colleges and universities
- Coaching and counseling
- Opportunities to attend seminars and conferences
- Apprenticeship programs
- Assignment of mentors or role models
- Transferring to other jobs to gain experience

Obviously, the training should be applied in as timely a manner as possible after the competency gaps have been identified. Allowing a significant amount of time to pass will only diminish the relevance of actions. Keep in mind that training is a complex undertaking and shouldn't be implemented randomly. Just like everything else in the management system, training must be carefully planned. Even on-the-job training must be well planned and carefully provided. In fact, due to the wide range of variables that interact in the job environment, on-the-job training usually requires even more planning. The planning will specify time frames, expectations, and measures.

It's vital that the trainee has a clear understanding of why the training is necessary and how it relates to job competency. If there has been effective communication, nobody will ever be heard saying, "They sent me to this training, but darned if I know why!" Communication should also portray training as a two-fold opportunity: It allows employees to increase their skills and knowledge and possibly broaden their career options, and it provides an avenue for the organization to invest in one of its most important resources and pave the way for its long-term success. If presented and delivered in this way, training becomes the epitome of a win-win relationship.

Ensure necessary competence has been achieved

Once training is complete, the organization must ensure that its goal—employee competence—has been met. This evaluation can take place in a number of manners, but the most obvious is a demonstration of the newly developed skills or abilities. This works especially well for competency building aimed at skills and training. "OK, we've talked about the task, and we've demonstrated how it should be performed. Now you give it a try." If the trainee is able to effectively perform the task while being observed, then he or she could be reasonably considered competent. Keep in mind that the observation period could be an hour, a day, a week, or a month. It all depends on the complexity of the skill being demonstrated. Most on-the-job training programs focus on this kind of evaluation. The trainee starts out as an apprentice and then gradually begins performing many of the tasks independently. The training culminates in the trainee being able to demonstrate the full range of skills involved with the job.

The inspection of an employee's work or product can verify that competence has been achieved. For employees who produce a tangible good or deliver a service, this is often a reasonable indicator of whether training has had the desired effect. Many organizations already have existing systems for inspecting their products. These systems can be channeled into the training program, but this will only work if the product's inspection is traceable back to individual employees.

Tests and examinations can be used to ensure competence, especially when the competence is related to knowledge and facts. Be aware that many individuals simply don't perform well on formal tests or examinations, regardless of the quality of the instruction and training materials, so this may not be an ideal gauge of effectiveness. Another drawback is that tests are heavy on administration, requiring someone to spend a great deal of time creating the tests, making sure that all learning objectives are addressed, creating answer keys and a grading scale, grading the tests, dealing with test anxiety and disappointment, and so on. However, tests and examinations have the advantage of resulting in a numerical score that is easy to quantify and track over time.

Finally, some organizations use performance reviews to judge whether employees are competent. Most organizations already use performance reviews of some sort. As long as a logical connection can be made between the training and the job performance, the system will work. One caution, however: Make sure to separate the record of performance review from the record of training effectiveness evaluation, as every organization seeking to keep or gain ISO 9001 registration will be required to provide evidence of the evaluation to its third-party auditor. Showing performance review records to outside parties will create ethical (as well as legal) problems, so you're far better off maintaining separate files.

In summary, here are some of the most common ways organizations ensure the competence of their personnel:

- Demonstration of skills and abilities
- Inspection of work output
- Written tests and examinations
- Performance reviews

Ensure that personnel understand how they contribute to objectives

ISO 9001 mandates awareness training on the relevance and importance of an employee's activities and how they contribute to achieving quality objectives. This is more complex than it sounds. Awareness training of this sort, when correctly applied, will have three results:

- Employees will have a full understanding of the measurable objectives their departments or functions are trying to achieve.
- Employees will understand how their actions—processing a loan, packing a box, or driving a forklift—contribute on a day-to-day basis in working toward their area's measurable objectives.
- Employees will gain a "big picture" understanding of the organization and its competitive environment, a perspective that is often lacking at all but the highest levels.

During an audit, it's common for personnel to be asked what objectives apply to their jobs and how they contribute to them. Make sure that everybody understands this in clear terms. It's important from the standpoint of an audit, but much more important from the standpoint of effective operations.

Maintain records

Record keeping is the last major issue to consider within the training program. ISO 9001 specifically requires records of four things: education, training, skills, and experience. This can be accomplished in a single record or four separate records. The fewer individual records, the better—particularly if the records are kept on paper. Make sure that all four of these variables are reflected on the record or records. Also, keep records of personnel's training on the "relevance and importance of (their) activities." Finally, the record of training effectiveness evaluation—another record that's not specifically required by the standard—is almost certainly required to demonstrate objective evidence of meeting the standard's requirements. Without the presence of a record, it will be virtually impossible to show that effectiveness was evaluated.

Electronic training records are a huge boon for many organizations. They clearly and quickly show what training has taken place or is due to take place and make gaps in training obvious. Anyone who has been through an ISO 9001 audit of paper training records will understand the pitfalls of this approach. The long-term costs of administering electronic records are usually much less than the costs of administering paper records, as well. If you do decide to take this route, make sure to maintain appropriate backup of all electronic files.

FREQUENTLY ASKED QUESTIONS

The president and CEO of our company is the owner. We have no ability to make him undergo training. Do we have to establish competency requirements for him?

Yes. Competency requirements must be established for all personnel who influence product quality, and this certainly applies to the president and CEO.

Do training records need to include the signatures of the people who were trained?

There is nothing in ISO 9001 that requires signatures on training records. There may be internal, statutory, or regulatory requirements that require signatures on training records, though.

> ***All our employees arrive at the organization fully competent, with significant experience, education, training, and skills. There's no additional training we need to provide. Is that OK?***
>
> At the very least, personnel need to be trained on the quality policy, quality objectives, and relevant aspects of your organization's quality management system. No amount of incoming competency will provide this type of information.
>
> ***Do we have to include temporary workers within our training process? Some of them are only with us a couple of days.***
>
> Yes, you must include all personnel who affect product quality. Exactly what the competency requirements are is up to you.

6.3 INFRASTRUCTURE

An organization's infrastructure is made up of the physical assets that enable it to produce its products. The specific assets will vary considerably, depending on the nature of your products. Here are some examples, based on a few different types of organizations:

- *Delivery company.* This type of firm relies heavily on assets that move product and store it securely. Thus, its critical infrastructure consists of trucks and warehouse facilities. The trucks are maintained under a service contract with a fleet maintenance company, and the warehouses are maintained by the real estate company they are leased from. As such, all maintenance is outsourced, but the effectiveness of maintenance is monitored on a regular basis. Any maintenance problems are reported to the outsourcing company that provides it and the organization is required to take corrective action. Once a year the company does a formal review of its maintenance providers and decides whether to continue its maintenance contracts.
- *Investment firm.* This firm relies heavily on infrastructure that provides and stores information. In other words, information technology (IT) is critical to its success. The firm has an IT department that maintains its computer hardware, software, and virus protection. There is also an IT trouble ticket process for users to report problems that require special attention. The IT department measures its effectiveness on how quickly it responds to maintenance needs.

■ *Manufacturing plant.* This organization uses large industrial equipment to produce its products. Each piece of equipment has a monthly, quarterly, and yearly maintenance program. The maintenance is scheduled so that equipment downtime is minimized so the plant exercises some discretion in the exact timing of the maintenance. The majority of the maintenance is performed by a centralized maintenance department, but some daily maintenance is performed by production personnel prior to beginning their work each day. The production and maintenance departments meet weekly to discuss the timing and effectiveness of maintenance and to revise maintenance schedules as needed.

Determine and provide infrastructure to achieve conformity

ISO 9001 provides some of its own examples of infrastructure. It lists such things as buildings, workspace, utilities, hardware, software, transport, and communication. As we've discussed, not all these assets are created equal. It's the responsibility of each organization to determine what its product-critical infrastructure consists of. ISO 9001 requires that you determine and provide the infrastructure needed to achieve conformity to product requirements. The key words are "needed to achieve conformity to product requirements." Whatever helps you do this is what you need to focus on from an infrastructure standpoint.

If your organization is producing products and satisfying customers it has already determined and provided infrastructure. The physical assets have already been acquired, at least on an initial basis. Determining and providing infrastructure isn't a one-time activity. It's something that must be revisited on a periodic basis as customers, products, and personnel change. Management review is a good opportunity to consider changes in infrastructure, as are strategic planning sessions, budgeting activities, and staff meetings. ISO 9001 doesn't require that you keep records of determining and providing resources, only that you do it. The more discipline you can build around infrastructure, though, the fewer problems will affect your operations.

Maintain infrastructure

ISO 9001 simply requires that your infrastructure be maintained. It doesn't require that you do this yourself, and it doesn't specify any frequencies or methods for maintenance. The entire program is up to you to design. As long as there is some sort of maintenance routine in place and there is evidence that it's effective, nobody has any right to challenge it.

You aren't required to document your maintenance program or schedules, but it would be a good idea to ensure that everyone is on the same page. Likewise, records are not explicitly required, but it would be difficult to prove that you're following your program without records. Strongly consider documenting your maintenance program and keeping records of fulfilling its requirements.

Just as the determination of infrastructure is not a one-time activity, the design of the maintenance program must be periodically revisited. The timing of maintenance, specific activities, and competence of maintenance personnel are likely to change periodically. Make the effectiveness of your maintenance process one of your measurable objectives and monitor it. Exactly what the objective is will obviously differ, depending on the type of maintenance being performed and the requirements that the organization has set.

Preventive and predictive maintenance

ISO 9001 doesn't require, or even mention, preventive or predictive maintenance. It simply requires maintenance, period. The specific type of maintenance program you implement is up to you. Common sense dictates that preventive and predictive maintenance are good ideas. They lower the overall costs of maintenance and increase the availability and productivity of equipment. Should you decide to implement a more robust approach to maintenance, that's the system against which you will be audited within the scope of your management system. Don't let this discourage you from doing what makes sense for your business.

FREQUENTLY ASKED QUESTION

Our organization is located in a rented office. The landlord takes care of all maintenance. What should we do about the infrastructure requirements of ISO 9001?

In the case of an office environment, the office building is likely to be less important than the equipment within the building. Focus on things like the computer system, telephones, and other infrastructure that are needed to produce your products within the office environment. Also, make sure you have communicated your building requirements to the landlord.

6.4 WORK ENVIRONMENT

An organization's work environment is made up of the conditions that exist in its workplace. The specific conditions that ISO 9001 is concerned about are those required to achieve conformity of product requirements. Examples of environmental conditions include configuration of the work area, employee health and safety, lighting, temperature, humidity, noise, vibration, cleanliness, pest control, and contamination. The required work environment will vary greatly, depending on the product being produced. Consider the following examples:

■ *Candy manufacturer.* Raw materials are received into the facility and immediately moved into a climate-controlled storage area. The cleanliness of the storage area is immaculate. A weekly inspection is conducted to look for any evidence of pests. Raw materials are transported into the manufacturing area by personnel wearing white gloves and smocks, and all manufacturing is tightly controlled under good manufacturing practices. All outside doors and windows are kept closed and the housekeeping is very strict; even the garbage cans are clean and spotless. Nobody with any kind of illness is permitted inside the facility, and no jewelry is permitted. Once manufacturing is complete, the finished product is stored in an area that is maintained at 40° F, plus or minus 4°, and the gage used to monitor the temperature is calibrated. A weekly audit is conducted to evaluate the condition of finished product in inventory.

■ *Insurance company.* People are stationed at desks and perform work on computers and telephones. The office temperature is maintained at typical office conditions, which is usually a compromise between the women who like the office warmer and the men who like it cooler. Dress codes are enforced so personnel are not distracted in their work and to maintain a professional environment in the event customers visit. Personnel are not allowed to play music from their radios or computers, as the sound disturbs people in their work, even when played at low volume. Hot food items are restricted to the break rooms, as some employees were offended by the smells of certain foods that were consumed at desks. Personnel photographs are decorations are permitted in cubicles, but nothing that could constitute a threatening work environment is allowed. Everything about the office is maintained in a pleasant yet bland manner because this is the environment that was found to result in the highest productivity, lowest service defects, and fewest personnel problems.

■ *Paper mill.* The inside of the plant is very damp, and a half-inch of water is on most of the floors. Additionally, the nature of the production process is very hot in some areas, and the ambient temperature in the summer can reach more than 110° F. During winter months, temperatures in the warehouses are just a few degrees above freezing. For many years, the harsh environmental conditions were simply accepted as a given. The conditions didn't negatively affect the product, so management felt no need to change anything. Recently it became clear that employees were becoming ill at a higher than normal rate, however. The increased illnesses affected the mill's attendance rate, which in turn affected its ability to produce paper on schedule. Work conditions are being improved now that the link between the environment and product conformity was recognized.

In all these cases, the work environment is focused on what is needed for the product the organization produces. Sometimes organizations discover connections between the work environment and product conformity that they didn't know existed, as in the paper mill example. ISO 9001 simply says that you will determine the environmental conditions that you require. Whatever you require is what you will be expected to provide and maintain.

Here are some typical controls related to specific work environment variables:

- *Temperature and humidity*: Gages for monitoring, records of conditions, records of gage calibration, investigation of affected product when conditions fail to meet environmental requirements
- *Safety hazards*: Identification of hazards, prioritization of risks, procedures for job safety, monitoring of compliance, records of monitoring, corrective action on accidents and near misses, regular meetings to discuss safety issues
- *Lighting, noise, vibration*: Specifications for characteristics, procedures for maintaining specifications, ongoing measurement of characteristics, records of measurement, calibration of gages, records of calibration
- *Housekeeping*: Procedures for housekeeping, defined responsibilities, training of personnel, periodic audits of housekeeping, corrective action on nonconformities, signage to remind personnel of guidelines
- *Personal hygiene and behavior*: Documented policies for personnel, recurring training, monitoring by supervision, and counseling for employees

ISO 9001 does not require documented procedures or records related to work environment, though it usually makes sense to have such things. In cases where the organization establishes requirements for work environment, the only way to verify that the environmental conditions were met would be through records. Documentation would also be required to consistently communicate the work environment requirements and controls.

FREQUENTLY ASKED QUESTION

We have a gage that monitors the temperature of our warehouse, which must be maintained at 50° F, ±10 degrees. Does the gage have to be calibrated?

Yes. Because you've committed to a particular work environment, having accurate readings of that environment is necessary.

Chapter 5

ISO 9001 Section 7 Product Realization

S ection 7 of ISO 9001, Product realization, addresses your core business processes. These are the things you do to create your product, no matter what your product consists of. Whether you arrange flowers, handle insurance claims, teach children math, or manufacture rods, you have processes that produce your product. Section 7 is the heart of ISO 9001. Nearly everything else in the standard exists to support the things you do in section 7.

Product realization is the only section of ISO 9001 from which you can exclude requirements. The only reasonable justification for excluding something is because that requirement doesn't apply to your organization. You don't perform the activities in the requirement, and not doing so has no effect on your ability to provide conforming products. Requirements can't be excluded for the sake of convenience. For example, you can't say, "Our top management is stupid, so we excluded section 5." While this statement might be factual, it's not adequate justification.

A typical exclusion is clause 7.3, Design and development. If you simply carry out a service or manufacture a product to your customer's specifications, then what is there to design? Another exclusion that organizations sometimes make is clause 7.6, Control of monitoring and measuring devices, otherwise known as "calibration." If you have no measuring equipment, then there's nothing to calibrate. In the event you have exclusions from section 7, make sure to indicate them in your quality manual and provide justification.

7.1 PLANNING OF PRODUCT REALIZATION

Planning of product realization is all about how you arrange and establish your production process. You're probably thinking, "My organization has been around for many years, and we've already developed out production processes. Do we have to go back and do it again?" No, of course, you don't. You may have to formalize some of your processes, though. You know those checklists that sometimes get completed and sometimes not? They'll need to be consistently completed. You know those inspections that people do when they have time? They need to be done on time, every time. Note that ISO 9001 doesn't require these controls, they're specified by your organization. You plan your product realization so it enables you to consistently create products that meet requirements. No matter what your product is, some kind of planning is required. As with all the "dot one" sections of ISO 9001, most of what clause 7.1 addresses is covered in more detail later in section 7.

Planning of product realization is not a one-shot deal. Your organization must periodically re-examine product realization as circumstances change. Management review is a good place to do this, especially under the input "Changes that could affect the quality management system." When your products, customers, personnel, and other circumstances change, there's a good chance that your existing production process could be affected. This section of ISO 9001 asks you to make changes as necessary. It's very similar to subclause 5.4.2, Quality management system planning, but the focus here is on product realization.

ISO 9001 lists a number of things you should consider related to product realization, as appropriate. Each of these is explained below.

Quality objectives and requirements for the product

It's impossible to have effective product realization if you don't really understand your product. This clause advises you to define your product in clear and unambiguous terms. In some cases, you may even specify quality objectives for different products. These are measurable goals related to the performance or conformity of certain products, established on an as-needed basis. This clause doesn't require you to establish quality objectives for all your products. You'll set objectives as you see fit. Subclause 5.4.1 states, "objectives, including those needed to meet requirements for product, are set..." This implies that you'll have at least one objective related to product. Beyond that it's up to you.

The other half of this clause requires you to define the requirements for your product. This can be done through a specification, drawing, blueprint, service order, schedule, or any number of other ways. Because all of these are subject to revision, they are documents and subject to document control. This requirement is closely related to 7.5.1a, which requires information that "describes the characteristics of the product."

Establish documents, processes, and resources for the product

Your planning will also determine the processes necessary to produce your product. These processes are nothing more than your methods and controls for making good product. If you examine your production process and think of the things that can go wrong, the controls become clear. If the methods and controls are important to be documented, they will be covered by document control. If they are not documented, you should have a good reason why not. Intensive training of personnel could be one reason. Most organizations will decide that documenting methods and controls is a good idea.

Resources enable product realization. They could include materials, supplies, tools, equipment, personnel, buildings, or just about anything else. You may recall us discussing resources of this sort in clause 6.3, Infrastructure. If you've already determined resources for product realization, there's no reason to do it again. Think about resources from the standpoint of those who actually have to create the product. This is often a radically different perspective than the people who make the resource decisions.

Required verification, validation, monitoring, measurement, inspection, and testing

All products get checked in some way. The check can be simple or complex, proactive or reactive, but you'll generally do something to make sure your product meets requirements. ISO 9001 uses a long list of potential checks (verification, validation, etc.), but it's up to you to decide what's necessary and when. People often find it helpful to think about product verification in different stages for planning purposes:

■ *Incoming.* This is the verification of purchased product. It can be very simple or quite complex, depending on the nature of the incoming product. Keep in mind that purchased product can be a good or a service, and the type of verification is likely to be different for each.

■ *In-process.* Before the good or service is completed, it often makes sense to perform a verification. This can prevent later problems and allow for correction in midstream.

■ *Final.* When the good or service is complete, a final inspection often adds value.

In the case of goods, this usually takes place before shipping of the product. In the case of services, it happens at the point of service delivery, often through the perceptions of the customer.

Just decide what makes sense for your given circumstances and plan the activity. We'll address this topic in more detail in subclause 8.2.4, Monitoring and measurement of product.

Records needed to provide evidence

This clause requires you to have proof that your product realization processes meet requirements. This doesn't mean you must keep records of everything. Rather, keep records of the formal checks you established for the preceding clause. If you explicitly commit to checking something, then the only way to demonstrate that you've done it is through records. If the checks were really needed, you'll want records indicating that your plans were properly executed.

The output of planning shall be in a suitable form

The output of all this planning we've been talking about is usually the management system itself. Your policies, procedures, and records are tangible results that planning took place. You don't have to produce a document titled "Plan for Product Realization" or "Quality Plan." Just plan your production process, then think about the procedures, processes, objective, resources, and records that will be needed to achieve conforming product.

If someone asks to see your planning for product realization, show them your management system documents related to production. Planning is how you knew what you needed. It's that simple.

7.2 CUSTOMER-RELATED PROCESSES

The majority of requirements related to customer management are located in this section. The one notable exception is customer satisfaction, which can be found in subclause 8.2.1. Customer-related processes are typically implemented in the customer service and sales areas of the organization. For organizations that don't deal directly with outside customers, these requirements are often addressed by scheduling or planning functions. Since all organizations have customers of some sort, it wouldn't be possible to claim an exclusion to this section. Applying the requirements of 7.2, Customer-related processes, may seem like a stretch for some organizations, but remember who your customers are. You certainly have customers, and these are the entities at whom you will focus these requirements.

7.2.1 Determination of requirements related to the product

This is where you take orders and determine product requirements. As I mentioned above, this typically takes place in customer service, sales, contracting, or somewhere else where personnel interact directly with customers. However, the process of defining product requirements can take place anywhere. Here are just a few of the many ways that you could determine product requirements:

- Taking orders via telephone, e-mail, or fax
- Receiving automated orders via the Internet
- Negotiating contracts
- Receiving a production schedule
- Agreeing to a project plan

The customer you're determining requirements with may be internal or external to your organization. Product requirements are often determined through a production schedule, project plan, work order, or similar tool for organizations that serve a different part of the same company

ISO 9001 requires you to define product requirements from four different angles. Let's look at each one of these and describe what each might involve.

Requirements specified by the customer

This is what the customer has explicitly asked for. There are usually some key performance issues that customer request. These differ widely by organization, but here are some of the most common:

- Product or service description
- Performance requirements
- Price
- Quantity
- Timing
- Location of product or service delivery
- Post-delivery activities

These requirements can be captured via telephone, fax, e-mail, Web form, electronic data interchange (EDI), or in person. The exact mode doesn't really matter as much as its ability to capture exactly what the customer wants. Having a form of some sort that probes the relevant issues (product description, performance requirements, etc.) will help ensure that all relevant attributes have been addressed. Assuming nothing about what the customer wants is also a good idea.

Requirements not stated by the customer but necessary

Customers don't bother to tell you all of their requirements. They assume certain things will be done, and then don't even think about other requirements. It's the organization's job to fill in the blanks and define the requirements not stated by the customer. These are often addressed through internal specifications or standards for your products. Unless the customer requests otherwise, the internal specification will supplement their requirements. Here are some examples of requirements not stated by the customer, but necessary for specified or intended use:

■ *Cleanliness.* Service providers often have internal guidelines for providing a clean product. This is the case for most hotels. Hotel customers, when making their reservations, would rarely ask that their bathroom be cleaned and the carpet vacuumed. This is simply expected, and anything else would not be acceptable to the customer.

■ *Packaging.* Customers rarely specify a particular type of packaging for products; they simply expect the product to arrive undamaged. The organization must determine the specific type of packaging that will adequately protect the product, and this becomes an internal specification for the organization.

■ *Professionalism.* Personnel acting on behalf of your organization are expected to behave professionally. They might be expected to dress in clean clothes, bathe, and speak properly when interacting with customers. A customer would rarely think to specify, "Please don't send any consultants to us that smell bad or swear a lot." It's simply expected that the organization has standards regarding professionalism. Failing to have these standards could certainly affect the conformity of the organization's product.

Think about the things your customer needs related to the product, but hasn't thought to specify. These are the attributes addressed by this clause of ISO 9001.

Statutory and regulatory requirements applicable to the product

Technically, there is a difference between statutory and regulatory requirements. It's a very fine difference, though. We'll cover it briefly for the sake of completeness. Statutes are laws. They say what you can and can't do in broad terms. Regulations are usually specific guidelines published and enforced by regulatory bodies. The bottom line is that statutes and regulations are both enforced by authorities that can make your life difficult. Understand what statutes and regulations apply to your products, and make sure you're able to meet them. Satisfaction of this clause is typically achieved in a two-part manner:

1. Developing a process for understanding and staying up-to-date with statutes and regulations

2. Compiling an index or listing of statutes and regulations applicable to your products

These processes aren't specifically required by ISO 9001, but they would represent an effective way of meeting the requirement.

It's worth noting that statutes and regulations can come from the country in which you are based, and they can originate from countries in which you're selling your products. Multinational organizations have to consider statutory and regulatory requirements everywhere they operate in the world. Understanding and staying current with statutes and regulations can become somebody's full-time job for companies that operate around the globe.

This clause is also very significant for companies that produce highly regulated products. Examples of highly regulated products include:

- Drugs and pharmaceuticals
- Medical devices
- Food
- Aircraft and aircraft parts
- Explosives and firearms

Address the requirement for statutory and regulatory requirements in the simplest way possible, but keep in mind that for certain organizations this will be a very strategic process.

Any additional requirements determined by the organization

Not all product requirements come from the customer, necessity, or the law. Some come from the organization, because it has deemed them appropriate. Many of these requirements fall into the categories of aesthetics and branding. Here are some examples of these categories:

- *Use of logos.* Many organizations require that their logo be affixed to the product and product packaging. There's no functional reason for doing this; it's simply a requirement that the organization determined to reinforce its branding.
- *Uniforms.* Personnel at service companies often wear uniforms. There is rarely any functional reason for this. It's simply a matter of branding and appearance.
- *Collection of feedback.* Some service organizations require that customer feedback be collected at the point of service. This certainly isn't essential to the product itself, but the organization has determined it to be necessary. Because the feedback is collected at the point of service, this is essentially another product requirement.
- *Distribution of marketing materials.* Many organizations include marketing materials when a good or service is delivered. This typically isn't required or requested by the customers, but the organization has made it an internal requirement.

How do all these requirements get documented? We've just discussed product requirements from four different perspectives. ISO 9001 simply requires that you determine these product requirements, but it doesn't provide any guidance on where these go once they've been determined. This is because each organization is likely to have its own way of capturing and communicating product requirements. In a perfect world, all product requirements would be shown clearly in one place. Despite this constant striving for simplicity, this is rarely the way things work. Product requirements are likely to be in more than one place, but as long as you can demonstrate that the requirements are accessible and complete, you have fulfilled the spirit of this element.

FREQUENTLY ASKED QUESTION

Do we have to put all the product requirements in the same place? They won't all fit on our sales order.

You don't have to record all the product requirements in the same place. As long you know what they are and can access them, then there's proof that they were determined.

7.2.2 Review of requirements related to the product

Once you determine product requirements, you must review them. This is really nothing more than a sanity check: Do we understand the requirements and can we really meet them? Most people have had experiences with organizations that promised to do something but badly missed the mark. The intent of this element is to keep you from being one of those organizations.

ISO 9001 requires that you review the order or contract prior to accepting it. In practical terms, this is the acceptance of the order or contract into your own system. The customer may have already placed the order, but you haven't formally accepted it into your system. This review can be performed by anyone, even the person who took the order in the first place. Specifically, the review includes three things:

■ *Product requirements are defined.* Have you accurately captured all the requirements related to the order or contract? The easiest way to do this is to simply look the order over and make sure the necessary details are present. Review often includes a check to ensure the following details are clearly defined, as appropriate:

☐ Product code or identification

☐ Product description

☐ Specifications and tolerances

☐ Engineering drawing, graphics, and blueprints

☐ Quantities

☐ Price (including currency to be used)

☐ Contract start and end dates

☐ Product delivery date

☐ Special requirements

☐ Customer address and contact information

☐ Legal requirements (indemnification, waivers, etc.)

For very complex orders or contracts, checklists are often used to ensure that all relevant details are covered. Tailor the review to your own special needs related to satisfying your customers.

■ *Requirements differing from those previously expressed are resolved.* It's not uncommon for an order or contract to involve many exchanges of information, some of which conflict with one another. This is especially true in this age of multiple communication channels. The more communication that takes place—especially among different modes and with different parties—the greater the chance that details will become confused. Just compare all the different communications that may have taken place and make sure that there aren't any conflicts. Here are some examples of how requirements can differ from those previously expressed:

☐ Specifications that accompany the order don't match the specifications on file.

☐ The customer placed an order via telephone and purchase order, but the purchase order requirements differ from the telephone order requirements.

☐ Two different customer representatives are asking for contradictory requirements.

☐ The customer requests different delivery dates.

☐ The customer asks you to do something that isn't in the contract.

If you encounter instances when requirements differ, contact the customer and resolve the conflict. Of course, keep a record of contacting the customer and what the final agreement was.

■ *The organization has the ability to meet the requirements.* It's not enough to understand the product requirements; you must be able to meet them. Scan the order or contract and make sure you're able to meet all the requirements. Here are some typical problems with "ability to meet defined requirements":

☐ Can't meet promised date

☐ Can't fulfill quantity

☐ Spare parts not available

☐ Qualified personnel not available

☐ Back-ordered supplies

☐ Rush orders from more important customers

☐ Equipment down for maintenance

☐ Supplier problems

☐ Labor unrest

☐ Terms and conditions are unacceptable

☐ Customer asks company to do something illegal

The bottom line is this: If you can't meet the requirements, don't accept the order. Customers will only take their business elsewhere if you commit to things you can't accomplish. Even worse, they will tell their friends and colleagues that you make promises you can't keep.

■ *Recording the review of product requirements.* You must keep a record of the review of product requirements. This record can be a signature, initials, stamp, form, or any other simple indicator. It is often affixed directly to the order or contract. Personnel working within the system should understand what constitutes the record of review and what it represents. Simply having a copy of the order or contract doesn't constitute a record of its review.

■ *Undocumented statement of requirements.* If the customer doesn't provide a documented statement of requirements, as is the case with telephone orders, you must confirm the order back to the customer. This can be as simple as repeating the requirements back to the customer to make sure you understood what he or she wanted. Some organizations go as far as to fax or e-mail the order to customers so they can review it themselves.

■ *Changes to requirements.* Orders and contracts are rarely static. They often evolve and change during the course of their lives. When product requirements change, make sure to amend the relevant documents. These could include work orders, travelers, specifications, schedules, or other documents. Failing to amend these documents can have huge negative consequences. Besides just amending relevant documents, you must have a system for communicating the changes to people who need to know. The communication can take place through the amended documents or through other means such as meetings, telephone calls, and e-mails.

FREQUENTLY ASKED QUESTION

We don't take orders or write contracts with customers. All we do is work against a schedule our home office sends to us once a week. Can we exclude the requirement of reviewing product requirements?

No. The schedule represents your product requirements (at least in part) and you must review them.

7.2.3 Customer communication

Customer communication should come naturally, but it rarely does. Organizations must develop explicit processes for customer communication to ensure that it takes place effectively. ISO 9001 does not require that processes for customer communication be documented, but organizations may decide that it's necessary to control them. Three explicit channels of customer communication are required by ISO 9001: product information, inquiries and changes, and feedback. Let's briefly discuss each one.

Product information

If you weren't already communicating about your products, you wouldn't have any customers. It's the most natural kind of communication imaginable. ISO 9001 simply requires that you determine and implement an effective process for communicating about product requirements. Here are some of the most common ways of communicating about products:

■ Service agreements
■ Product data sheets
■ Marketing literature and brochures
■ Web sites
■ Price lists
■ Product samples

The most common problem with product information is that it isn't maintained to keep it current. Make sure you have an effective process for communicating product information and keeping it up to date. Incorrect product information is a frequent cause of customer complaints, so it clearly has an effect on your success.

Inquiries, order handling or contracts, and amendments

After you provide product information, the next step is (hopefully) an order. This clause asks you to determine communication that will effectively manage the transaction. Here are a few words about each type of the transactional communication:

■ *Inquiries.* How do customers inquire about the availability of product or other information? Sure, you've already provided product information, but it's common for people to have additional questions. Sales people or operators often receive inquiries, but they can also be handled by an automated system. Typical ways of handling inquiries include telephone, e-mail, Web site, database query, or in person. The process for making an inquiry is usually defined within product information.

■ *Order handling or contracts.* How does someone place an order or initiate a contract? If there is one kind of communication you want to make simple and intuitive, it's this one. After all, someone is trying to give you money. How difficult do you want to make it? Often the method for placing an order is the same as the method for placing an inquiry, but not always. Clearly specify the method for initiating business and keep the information up to date.

■ *Amendments.* This is one type of communication that organizations often forget to establish. It acknowledges that customers sometimes change their minds and make mistakes. Most organizations establish time limits for amendments, beyond which a customer is obligated for at least a portion of the cost of the order or contract. You need to let customers know how to amend their orders, and clearly communicate the rules and penalties (as applicable).

Customer feedback, including customer complaints

How does your organization receive customer feedback and complaints? Let your customers know the methods and make it as easy as possible. This is especially the case with complaints. Try to avoid complicated processes that discourage dialogue and frustrate customers. Smart organizations remind their customers on a regular basis of how to provide feedback and post complaints. The topic of customer feedback is addressed in much more detail in subclause 8.2.1 of ISO 9001.

FREQUENTLY ASKED QUESTION

We have effective means of communicating with our customers, including a toll-free phone number, Web site, and frequent meetings. Do we need to document these processes in a procedure?

No, not unless you think it adds value.

7.3 DESIGN AND DEVELOPMENT

This section of the standard addresses the design of your product. It doesn't specifically address design of a process, although the requirements could certainly be applied to that type of activity. At a minimum, you must meet the requirements in the design of products, if you perform design. Many organizations exclude this requirement because they simply fulfill customer requirements and no design is performed.

Before you happily declare, "We don't do design!" let's discuss it a little further. Here are some criteria for deciding if you are actually designing and developing:

- If you are producing a unique good or service for which your customer has not provided specifications, then you may be doing design and development.
- If your customer has only given you vague performance requirements and asked you to come up with a good or service that will meet those requirements, then you may be doing design and development.
- If your product is driven by your organization's powers of creativity and innovation, then you may be doing design and development.
- If one or more of your products is protected by patents, then you may be doing design and development.

Clearly, there are exceptions to each of these cases above. The good news is that design and development can be very simple. In its essence, it's nothing more than project management: breaking a complex process into more manageable activities. Let's examine each of the steps and explain what they require.

FREQUENTLY ASKED QUESTION

Do we need to keep separate records of each stage of design? We would like to combine all of these into a single record, sort of like a "design traveler" that follows a new product through the entire design process.

You can format your design records in whatever way makes sense to you. The record you described sounds like it could work very well.

7.3.1 Design and development planning

The design plan is the path you expect to take in creating the design. Given your knowledge of the product's complexity, what tasks will need to be involved? Who will need to take part and how long will the process take? What resources will be needed? The design plan will be your road map for the remainder of the process.

The plan can take many forms, from highly sophisticated to very simple. The trick is to match the design plan to the nature of the product being designed. Some design plans are little more than a memo or a flow diagram. For more complex products, the design plan may comprise many documents, including a Gantt chart, critical path, work breakdown structure, and other project management tools. Regardless of what it looks like, it will be a document, with all the controls that go along with a document. We know this because ISO 9001 says that the plan will be updated as design and development progresses, and only documents are updated.

Only use as much planning as you need. Remember, the purpose of design planning is to help you manage the design process, and there's no extra credit for being fancy or using complicated tools. The way you achieve design planning is completely up to you. Your design plan will typically address a number of variables:

- *Participants and responsibilities.* Who exactly will be involved with this design? What will they be expected to do? Do the participants understand and accept their responsibilities?
- *Interfaces.* With whom should the persons with design responsibilities interface or interact? Nobody works in isolation (or at least they shouldn't), and it's important to drive as much communication and interaction as possible.

■ *Resources.* What funds, facilities, equipment, supplies, and other resources will be needed to carry out this design? Have the resources been secured? If not, where will they come from?

■ *Major tasks.* What major tasks must be performed to produce the design? In what sequence should these tasks be performed? Keep in mind that major tasks will include verifications and validations of the design (both of which are discussed later in this chapter).

■ *Deliverables.* What are the deliverables or products of each task? How will we know that the task has been accomplished?

■ *Timing of tasks and deliverables.* When are tasks due to be completed? When will the deliverables be produced?

■ *Reviews.* How will the organization review progress on the design? Who will be involved in the reviews? When will the reviews take place?

■ *Verification(s).* Exactly what attributes of the design will be evaluated during design verification? How will the design be verified? Who will perform verification?

■ *Validation(s).* What attributes, features, and performance properties of the design will be evaluated during validation? How will validation be performed? Who will perform it?

For some organizations, the design plan is basically the same each time they design something. It's a routine process, with the only difference being the specific timing of the tasks. Organizations that design variations of the same kind of product often fall into this category. In these cases, there's no reason to make the design plan any more complicated than it needs to be. A simple template with spaces for the dates to be filled in works very well.

7.3.2 Design and development inputs

Inputs tell us what design and development must satisfy. The inputs may come from market research, customer feedback, sales reports, or pure speculation. Regardless of the source, ISO 9001 outlines four things that must be included as inputs:

■ *Functional and performance requirements.* How should the product function? What must it be able to do? What resources must be available to support it? What are the product's limitations?

■ *Applicable statutory and regulatory requirements.* What laws govern the production and use of your product? Are there any regulatory guidelines related to your product? How do these issues affect the design process?

■ *Information derived from previous similar designs.* There is a chance that your organization has designed a similar good or service in the past. Apply lessons learned in the earlier design to the current project.

■ *Other requirements essential for design and development.* These are requirements that aren't addressed by the other three categories. They could include the cost of the product (material cost, labor cost, etc.), appearance attributes, compatibility with other goods and services, use of logos or trademarks, ability to be produced using particular equipment or personnel, and other factors.

Design inputs are often captured in meeting minutes, memos, design worksheets, market summaries, and sometimes on cocktail napkins. Wherever they are captured, they must be reviewed for adequacy. This is easily accomplished through signatures, initials, or other approval means. The design inputs are usually considered a record, as they indicate what the organization required at a particular time.

7.3.3 Design and development outputs

Design output is the product of the design process. The design output defines exactly what the organization will produce to meet the design input requirements. The output takes the input and turns it into something your organization can provide. Design output always takes the form of documentation of some sort. Here are some examples:

■ Sketches
■ Engineering drawings
■ Blueprints
■ Product specifications
■ Service instructions
■ Bills of materials
■ Manufacturing instructions
■ Installation instructions
■ Specifications for components, subassemblies, raw materials, or other purchased products
■ Packaging and labeling specifications
■ Handling and storage specifications
■ Appearance standards

■ Safety warnings, labels, and reminders
■ Consumer or user instructions
■ Troubleshooting and repair guides
■ Flowcharts
■ Calculations
■ Computer code
■ Operating criteria
■ Physical specimens or prototypes

The format and style of design outputs are only limited by the organization's power of imagination. Regardless of what the design outputs look like, there are a number of requirements the organization must satisfy:

■ *Meet input requirements.* The whole point of design output is to guide the organization in producing a new or improved product. To do this, the outputs must clearly meet the input requirements. All the relevant requirements outlined by the Inside/Out Review must be satisfied within the output(s). This has a great deal of value, as it ensures that the organization keeps its eyes on the expectations of its customers and the marketplace as it goes through the design process.

■ *Provide information for purchasing, production, and service provision.* Design outputs are communication tools. Their primary function is to tell everyone what to do to make the new product a success. As such, they must provide information to functions like purchasing, logistics, production, quality assurance, and sales. That's one of the reasons there may be multiple design outputs: They are tailored to a wide variety of functions.

■ *Contain or reference acceptance criteria.* The outputs must indicate what constitutes the acceptable attributes of the product. In other words, what specific requirements must the product meet? Examples of acceptance criteria may include dimensional tolerances, performance specifications, material properties, aesthetic requirements, and a very wide range of other possible issues. The nature of the product clearly dictates what kind of acceptance criteria will apply. Note that acceptance criteria not only applies to the design of goods, but also to services that the organization designs.

■ *Specify the characteristics of the product that are essential for its safe and proper use.* Customers are often very creative in the way they use products, especially new products. Occasionally, they even use products in ways that could lead to injury or death. The design outputs must clearly indicate the safe and appropriate use of the product. Doing this protects the organization and its customers. Organizations that have failed to perform this step with due diligence often find themselves facing costly lawsuits, bankruptcy, and criminal prosecution.

Design outputs logically lead to the next stage of design control, which is design review.

7.3.4 Design and development review

Design reviews are the way you make sure the design is proceeding according to plan. All designs have at least one design review, and complex designs may have many more. There's no particular magic to the number of design reviews. If the design process has a great deal of complexity and risk, there will need to be more design reviews. One of the key planning activities is to decide how many design reviews are appropriate for the particular product being designed.

Purposes of design review

ISO 9001 specifies two main purposes of the design review:

■ Evaluate the ability of the results of design and development to meet requirements.
■ Identify any problems and propose necessary actions.

The design review is a reality check to ensure that everything is on track. If it's not, it will be revealed at the design review and appropriate action can be taken to fix the problem before it throws the entire project off schedule. Design reviews must be action-oriented to be effective. ISO 9001 also requires records of design reviews and any necessary actions.

Participants in design review

Participants in design reviews are those involved in the design stage being reviewed. Typical participants include designers, engineers, production managers, purchasing personnel, and logistics managers. Later in the design process, reviews may also include marketing, sales, and senior management. The point is to get the people who understand the variables of design together and review the status of all the design tasks. The design review doesn't have to be a physical meeting. It could be performed via teleconference or through other remote means. As long as the participants have access to necessary information relating to design progress, it doesn't really matter if everyone is together in the same room. Face-to-face dialogue can be helpful, however, especially when problems must be resolved.

Typical agenda

Each design review should be conducted according to a structured agenda. Don't leave the content of the design review up to the participants' discretion. Publish the agenda in advance and make sure all participants are prepared to contribute. This isn't a requirement of ISO 9001, but it sure makes the review go smoother.

The following actions are typically addressed during a design review:

- Evaluate progress on the design.
- Compare progress against the design plan.
- Agree on actions needed to close gaps.
- Identify resources to be procured or re-aligned.
- Revise the design plan, if necessary.
- Provide feedback and encouragement to designers.
- Identify risks and roadblocks that have appeared, and decide how they will be managed.
- Confirm that the design is ready to move on to the next stage.
- Ensure that the design is staying focused on the design inputs.

7.3.5 Design and development verification

Design verification ensures that the design outputs meet the design inputs. It's basically an inspection activity, but one of the most critical inspection activities an organization can perform. Verification may be performed once near the end of the design process or it may be done at multiple times as incremental design outputs are generated. It all depends on the nature of the product being designed. Complex products will almost always require more than one design verification.

Verification topics

ISO 9001 doesn't provide much guidance on what should be covered during design verification. It simply says that you should ensure outputs meet input requirements. Your inputs could cover nearly anything relevant to the product being designed. Here are some topics that possibly could be addressed during design verification:

■ *Confirmation of basic attributes.* This is the most routine type of verification. It simply involves a comparison of the requirements shown on design inputs against the attributes reflected on the output documents. Attributes that could be verified in this manner include size, shape, weight, color, and configuration.

■ *Verification of performance properties.* This is a much more robust type of verification. Performance properties may include speed, strength, hardness, durability, reliability, and many other qualities. These properties typically can't be checked off in a mechanical fashion like basic attributes; calculations, simulations, or computer modeling may need to be utilized in order to know whether the performance requirements in the inputs have been satisfied by the outputs. Remember that these performance properties are shown on design output documents.

■ *Tests of prototypes.* Design outputs sometimes include prototypes of the product being designed. In these cases, verification may include actual tests of the prototype's physical properties. We've now moved away from verifying documents to verifying something that the customer would recognize as a real product. The way the prototype differs from a real product is that it's not produced under typical production conditions. The prototypes are produced under careful conditions probably unlike those that will be present when the design goes into full production. Testing the prototype can still provide valuable insights.

■ *Comparison to similar designs from the past.* History is a powerful source of knowledge, but it's often overlooked. When verifying design outputs, it's helpful to refer to earlier designs that have similar attributes and performance properties. How well does the current design shape up to designs of the past? Have we incorporated all the lessons learned from the earlier designs? Do we have customer feedback on earlier designs that needs to be incorporated into the current design?

■ *Safety and health review.* Verification should carefully consider the safety and health aspects of the product being designed. The design inputs will provide direction on the applicable considerations, but sometimes it's difficult early in the process to know with certainty what safety and health issues apply. For that reason, design verification should apply a wide ranging evaluation of all possible safety and health issues, just to make sure that nothing has been neglected. Unsafe or unhealthy products will doom the organization, no matter how innovative the products are.

■ *Environmental impact review.* Every product used or produced has an environmental impact. It's a truth that is beyond argument. The question is not whether the new product causes environmental impacts, but how severe are the impacts. The design outputs must be verified to ensure that they meet all applicable environmental laws. Just as important, the outputs should be verified to ensure that unregulated impacts aren't being generated in excess quantities. A full life cycle review of the product, its packaging, and the associated supplies is a robust way to verify the environmental impact of the product being designed.

■ *Marketing review.* Nearly everything we've mentioned so far about design verification has been technical in nature. However, we can't lose sight of the whole purpose of design: to meet a need in the marketplace. The organization's marketing specialists should be involved in the design verification to ensure that nothing identified in the design inputs is forgotten, particularly in the case of subtle or highly nuanced requirements.

■ *Legal review.* In the United States, a company can be sued for almost anything. Grounds for filing suit range from the gravely serious to the ridiculous. The very nature of a new or improved product means that the organization is venturing into a potentially risky and untried area of operation. Many product designs require legal staff to be involved in the verification process so that these risks are properly managed.

Responsibility for performing verifications

Design verification can be performed by any qualified persons, inside or outside the organization. However, due to the confidential nature of most designs, verifications are typically performed inside the organization. Regardless of where the verifications take place, it's helpful if the verification is performed by an independent function. At the very least, avoid having designers verify their own work.

Changes to the design

There is always the chance that design verification will result in changes to the design. That's really the point: to ensure the design is meeting all requirements, and, if not, to make necessary changes. Changes can be triggered by any number of factors:

■ Failure to address input requirements
■ Misinterpretation of input requirements
■ Unsatisfactory test or simulation results

- Errors or omissions in the design
- Addition of lessons learned from earlier designs
- Unanticipated or unmet safety/health considerations
- Unanticipated or unmet environmental considerations
- Significant legal risks
- Addition of improved features or performance attributes

Records of design verification

Design verification always produces records. These records typically indicate who performed the verification, when it was performed, what specific parameters were verified, the results of the verification, and any actions that must be taken. The records can be quite simple, and often can be incorporated into other design records.

7.3.6 Design and development validation

Validation is similar to verification, except in the case of validation we no longer evaluate abstract representations of the product (e.g., drawings and specifications). Instead, we evaluate an actual version of the product itself. The product may be a production prototype, sample, beta test, pilot run, or first article, but essentially it's the same product that will be offered to customers. Validation sums up everything about the designed product and asks, "Will this product do everything it's supposed to do in the eyes of the customer?"

Design validation is one of the most important activities in the design control process. Why? Because it forces the organization to perform a reality check on its design work. It requires a deliberate, head-to-head examination of what the organization designed versus the customer's use in the real world. Spend the time and effort to perform design validation in a comprehensive manner.

Keys to successful validation

These are the four keys to successful validation:

- Evaluating the same product that customers will actually consume
- Evaluating the product in the same way customers will use or misuse it
- Evaluating the product in a holistic or cumulative manner, instead of only focusing on product attributes in isolation from one another
- Evaluating the production process to ensure it is truly capable of producing the new product

Don't make the mistake of validating a product that was produced by experts under carefully controlled conditions in a research-and-development laboratory. The validated product needs to be produced in the same way a product is produced for market consumption. All the typical production problems that arise when a product goes into day-to-day production should be considered. The organization shouldn't cherry pick its best materials, personnel, and equipment when producing a product for validation. The production conditions must be realistic.

Meeting requirements for specified application or intended use

Not only must the product be produced under realistic conditions, it must also be evaluated under realistic conditions. So, if we're designing golf carts, we'll take a cart for a spin on an actual golf course. Rain, shine, hot, and cold, just as a real golfer might. The organization also needs to try to anticipate ways the customer might misuse the product. Perhaps the golf cart isn't really intended to be driven through three inches of standing water, but that's exactly what golfers will do. Golfers may also be expected to spill beer on the seats and the dashboard. They may also try to drive the cart over curbs and other obstructions. Validation needs to include all of these uses and misuses.

Validation evaluates individual product features, of course. More important, it must summarize all the features and determine if the product as a whole meets requirements. Everyone has heard the old cliché, "More than a sum of its parts." The words are very accurate, cliché or not. The designed product is much more than a sum of its parts, and the validation should acknowledge this reality. The overall perceptions of the people performing validation are often more valuable than the results of individual evaluations.

The nature of design validation will differ drastically, depending on the product in question. Here are some examples of how different products may undergo validation:

- Pharmaceuticals: clinical trials
- Educational course: beta tests using volunteer students
- Automobile: road test trials, crash test trials, engineering tests
- Food and beverage: consumer taste tests, laboratory tests
- Kitchen appliance: multiple-cycle usage tests, consumer focus group

Completed prior to the delivery or implementation of the product

Ideally, the organization should validate the design of its products before releasing them to the market. However, sometimes this isn't possible. Certain products can't be validated under conditions of use without getting the customer involved. This is especially the case for large, custom-designed products designed for very specific applications. Whatever arrangement that allows you to simulate "specified application or intended use" is what you will use, and this may require validation in the open market.

Records of validation

Just like verification, validation produces records. The records should outline all the details of the validation: the manner of validation, the conditions under which it took place, exactly what features or attributes were validated, who performed it, and when it took place. The typical rules of records apply here: keep them simple and as concise as possible.

7.3.7 Control of design and development changes

This clause is applicable if your organization alters existing designs. When we change existing designs, we must perform many of the activities used in the original design. The changes must be reviewed, verified, validated (as appropriate), and approved.

When making changes to the design, it's important to consider whether the change could affect components of the product or product that has already been shipped. In terms of records, changes must produce design review records at minimum. A good argument could be made for also keeping records of verification and validation, although ISO 9001 doesn't explicitly require this. As with all verification and validation activities, there is no proof that these things are happening without records.

7.4 PURCHASING

Purchasing is an essential support function for most organizations. You have to buy goods and services to function. ISO 9001 doesn't provide any guidance on the types of purchases that will be addressed by this section. It's up to your organization to define the purchased products that have the most effect on your operations. Typical purchases that are considered "critical"—and which are managed through the purchasing requirements of ISO 9001—include:

■ Raw materials used to produce your product
■ Purchased components that become part of your product
■ Product packaging
■ Equipment used to provide a service
■ Mission-critical spare parts
■ Outsourced testing labs that verify your product
■ Transportation providers that deliver your goods or services
■ Calibration services
■ Providers of contract labor
■ Outsourced production processes

Again, it's up to your organization to define the purchases that will be managed through your purchasing process. Decide for yourself what's critical and manage those suppliers and relationships. It's worth noting that a number of the suppliers listed above could actually be considered outsourced processes. This is why most organizations manage their outsourcing through their purchasing process.

There's nothing wrong with controlling all purchasing through the requirements specified in clause 7.4. The only problem is that the return on investment becomes quite low when you begin evaluating suppliers of toilet paper and pencils.

Approved supplier list

ISO 9001 doesn't require the organization to create an approved supplier list. If you have committed to using only certain suppliers, then an approved supplier list (or something equivalent) might be very helpful. Of course, an approved supplier list would be a controlled document.

FREQUENTLY ASKED QUESTIONS

Can we evaluate our suppliers though a supplier questionnaire?

Yes, but weigh the value of a questionnaire against other types of criteria. Questionnaires are often "pencil whipped" by suppliers and seldom reflect meaningful performance of the suppliers.

> **Do we have to keep records of verifying purchased product?**
>
> Yes. Records are not specifically required in clause 7.4, but there would be no other way to demonstrate that the verification took place. Also, subclause 8.2.4 requires records of all monitoring and measurement of product, which would certainly include purchased product.

7.4.1 Purchasing process

Subclause 7.4.1 addresses the specific requirements around verifying purchased product and managing supplier performance.

Ensure purchased product meets requirements

Everything you buy (including services) must be verified in some manner to ensure it meets your requirements. The good news is that this is much easier to implement than it sounds. Different products will be subject to different levels of verification. For example, office supplies, can be verified through checking for correct quantity, correct identification, damage, and on-time delivery. More critical products—such as raw materials that go into a final product—might undergo lab tests, detailed visual inspection, and examination of statistical data. Services are likewise verified to ensure that they meet requirements. All of these verifications must result in records. The records can be quite simple. In the case of the simple check of quantity, identification, and condition, the record could be the inspector's signature and date on the packing slip or receiving ticket. In the case of lab tests, the resulting test data would serve as the record of verification.

The type and extent of control applied to the supplier

This clause gives the organization leeway in terms of how much control is applied to its suppliers: *"The type and extent of control applied to the supplier and the purchased product shall be dependent upon the effect of the purchased product on subsequent product realization or the final product."* In plain language, this means you will control mission-critical suppliers more stringently than less important ones. This highlights the practical nature of supplier management. The companies that supply pencils and paper may only get evaluated on whether the product shows up on time and undamaged. On the other hand, the companies that supply a critical raw material, may have to submit their products to stringent lab tests and their management system to periodic customer audits. The level of control all depends on how important the product is.

The organization shall evaluate and select suppliers

Selecting suppliers is a fairly straightforward task. Think about what drives your purchasing decisions when you're using your own money; the same criteria make sense for your company. Here are some common-sense selection factors:

- *Capability.* Does the supplier provide the type of product you're seeking? Are all necessary services, warranties, and information provided? If not, there's no sense in investigating the supplier further.
- *Availability.* Can the supplier provide the good or service in the time and location desired?
- *Pricing.* Is the price competitive, given the total package of services offered? It's important to note that the lowest price is often not the best deal.
- *Quality.* Can the supplier meet your specifications, tolerances, and performance requirements?
- *Solvency.* Will the supplier still be in business next month? How about next year? This is not necessarily a consideration for commodity items but is generally a requirement when warranties and product follow-up are part of the deal. You don't want to find a padlock on the supplier's door when you're in need of technical assistance or spare parts.

These are the most basic issues for selecting a supplier, and they are typically verified through research of the supplier candidate's sales literature, Web sites, published specifications, discussions with its representatives, industry journals, and customer references. Occasionally, the selection criteria may be verified through a trial purchase. This is the case when long-term contracts, large product quantities, or extremely critical products are involved. The trial purchase can reveal a great deal about what to expect over the long term.

Additional selection criteria can certainly be added, also. If the supplier becomes a vital business partner—supplying critical goods and services that have a direct bearing on your own success—then it makes sense to insist upon a formal management system. A formal management system will ensure a degree of customer focus, discipline, and problem prevention. If an accredited third party has registered the supplier's management system, this provides one more degree of oversight.

Some organizations see fit to introduce even more selection criteria, including:

- Environmental performance
- Minority ownership
- Diversity of the work force
- Safety practices
- High ethical standards
- Overall working conditions
- Use of child labor
- Employee harassment and abuse
- Freedom of association for employees

These criteria address a category that I will call public relations and organizational values. It's a difficult category for most organizations to evaluate. The organization is really trying to answer two simple questions:

- Will the supplier's business practices expose the organization to negative public relations, possibly leading to risk or liability (such as negative media reports, civil lawsuits, or criminal prosecution)?
- Are the supplier's business practices so contrary to our own values that we cannot in good conscience enter into a relationship with it?

The methods for answering these questions can be very complex. The most obvious method is to go on-site, or pay someone to go on-site on your behalf and verify compliance. Either of these options is expensive. An alternative is to require the organization to implement a management system model that reflects the variables you're most concerned about. Examples include SA8000 (the international social accountability standard), Worldwide Responsible Apparel Production (WRAP) certification, and ISO 14001 (for environmental management systems). These standards have the advantage of enabling the supplier to adapt its processes and procedures to established guidelines, ultimately allowing assessment and registration by a third-party auditor. The assessment and registration is at the supplier's expense, of course. This arrangement is by far the most efficient, and often the most effective, for organizations that want to introduce additional risk and values requirements to their business relationship with a supplier.

The bottom line is that organizations should only use supplier selection criteria that they really believe in and that they are prepared to verify. If either of these conditions is not met, then it's deceptive to both the supplier and the organization. It's also a waste of time and energy.

Define criteria for selection, evaluation, and re-evaluation

We've already discussed some typical criteria for selecting suppliers. You must communicate the criteria in a way that enables it to be implemented. In practical terms, this usually means it will be documented. ISO 9001 doesn't specifically require that you establish a documented procedure for purchasing, but it makes sense for many organizations.

The second type of criteria you must define is the one you use for evaluating suppliers. This is your ongoing process for monitoring supplier performance. Nearly any reasonable criteria can be used. The trick is applying meaningful measures that help you manage suppliers and improve their performance. The criteria for evaluating the supplier can be intertwined with your verification of the product it provides. In many ways, this is the most meaningful way to evaluate suppliers. Here are some typical evaluation criteria:

- *Timeliness.* Did the good or service arrive when it was supposed to?
- *Quantity.* Did the correct quantity arrive?
- *Location.* Did the good or service arrive at the correct location?
- *Identification.* Did the correct type of good or service arrive?
- *Condition.* Did the product arrive in the correct condition, with no damage or deterioration?
- *Achievement of requirements.* Did the good or service meet all the terms of the contract or order?
- *Test/inspection data.* Did the product arrive with the necessary test or inspection results, and do the results indicate that the product meets the requirements? (This may not be applicable to all products.)
- *Internal test results.* Does the product pass our internal tests or lab analyses? (This may not be applicable to all products.)
- *Performance.* Does the good or service perform satisfactorily in its intended application?
- *Billing.* Did the bill arrive when it was supposed to, and was it accurate?
- *Effectiveness.* Did the service accomplish what it was supposed to?
- *Courtesy.* Was the service person courteous?
- *Communication.* Was the service person or supplier representative able to communicate effectively?
- *Problem solving.* Was the service person or supplier representative able to diagnose and solve any problems?

The auditing of suppliers is occasionally promoted as a technique for evaluating and managing them. When performed correctly, auditing sends a very powerful message to the supplier and can drive significant improvements. However, it brings with it many obstacles, such as:

■ *Expense.* It's expensive to perform audits. Travel costs alone make this prohibitive for many organizations.

■ *Difficulty.* Think how difficult it is for your internal auditors to audit your own facility and draw valid conclusions. It is exponentially more difficult to audit someone else's facility and draw valid conclusions and drive improvements. Only the most experienced and skillful auditors can succeed in supplier audits.

■ *Logistics.* The logistics of trying to schedule audits is very complex. Agreeing on the date, time, scope, and agenda for an audit can take hours of back-and-forth communication between the organization and the supplier. Agreeing on how corrective actions will be handled is even more complex.

■ *Intrusiveness.* Suppliers are busy. Just like your organization, they barely have time in the day to take care of the most pressing issues. Being audited only constrains them further. Many suppliers resent this intrusion and will bear it only grudgingly.

If auditing is considered valuable, then compel suppliers to develop their own internal auditing functions. Even more desirable is to require that they work toward the development of a formal management system with the ultimate goal of recognition by a third-party registrar. This allows the supplier to be the master of its destiny, and it also lowers the costs and aggravations of supplier management. In cases where the benefits of auditing suppliers outweigh the obstacles, dedicate the time and energy into making sure it achieves the desired results. Don't approach the task lightly.

The third type of criteria you must define is the criteria for re-evaluating suppliers. This is a little bit confusing. Re-evaluation is the reconsideration of your organization using a particular supplier. In other words, it's clobbering time! Re-evaluation is nearly always triggered by something bad that the supplier did. If you have meaningful criteria for evaluating suppliers, then you'll know very quickly when they do something bad. Some situations that might trigger re-evaluation include:

■ Repeat problems
■ Blatant disregard of your requirements
■ Unprofessional conduct by the supplier
■ Over-billing
■ Failure to follow statutory or regulatory requirements
■ Criminal prosecution
■ Negative news reports

When you evaluate a supplier, you decide if you want to continue the business relationship. It's a very serious decision. What criteria are useful for re-evaluating suppliers? Here are some typical ones:

■ *Corrective action.* Issue the supplier a corrective action request, demanding investigation and action within a fixed time period. Failure to respond puts it at risk for losing its contract with you

■ *Supplier audit.* Another way of re-evaluating suppliers is to audit their operations. We've already talked about the challenges of auditing suppliers, but it can be an effective practice when faced with the decision of continuing the business relationship. When problems are identified during the audit, the supplier is issued corrective action requests and its responses to these are carefully monitored.

■ *Probation.* A third way of re-evaluating suppliers is to simply put them on "probation" within your purchasing system. Probation will usually subject them to reduced business and higher scrutiny for a length of time. If their performance improves during the probationary time, they will be removed from probation and reinstated as a normal supplier. If their performance does not improve during the probationary period, they are no longer used.

Records of the results of evaluations

When you evaluate a supplier, ISO 9001 requires that you maintain a record of the results. You must also record any necessary actions resulting from the evaluation. We described a wide range of methods for evaluating suppliers, so the records for these would also vary widely. Here are some guidelines for effective records:

■ *Incorporate them into existing paperwork.* If you already use a purchase order, incorporate your supplier evaluation into this tool. I have seen stickers, stamps, and other simple records used directly on the purchase order to indicate that the supplier was evaluated and how it performed against the criteria. Packing lists, receiving logs, and work orders can also be used to capture the evaluation.

■ *Use electronic records whenever possible.* If you have a computer system that receives purchased product, use this to record your supplier evaluation. Even if you don't have an automated system, a simple spreadsheet can record the details.

Both of these approaches are aimed at making the records as transparent as possible. If the creation of records is complex and time-consuming, you can bet it won't happen.

7.4.2 Purchasing information

This is a very simple section of ISO 9001, but it's written so that it appears very complex. Here's the simple version: *Tell your suppliers exactly what you want from them.* I told you it was simple. If you have a purchase order process, then it probably already requires full descriptions of the good or services requested, date needed, delivery location, price, billing terms, applicable specifications, and any other requirements. Even if you simply use e-mails to communicate requirements to suppliers, this system can be effectively used. However, the purchasing information requirement would be difficult to meet without some sort of record of what you have requested. From a strictly business standpoint, you would certainly want a record of what you have requisitioned from suppliers.

Ensure the adequacy of purchase requirements

The last statement in this section is clear: Ensure the adequacy of purchase requirements before communicating with suppliers. This is a common-sense requirement, as smart people rarely communicate something before checking the message for completeness, accuracy, and clarity. That's all this requirement is asking you to do. The only way to prove that you checked something is to maintain a record of having done it. With a purchase order, a signature is typically adequate proof of having ensured the adequacy of purchase requirements.

7.4.3 Verification of purchased product

Ensure that purchased product meets requirements. This element addresses your methods for checking, inspecting, or otherwise ensuring that what you ordered is indeed what you received. It's a repeat of the requirement that begins subclause 7.4.1. The words "inspection or other activities" are specifically mentioned here, meaning you could do an inspection or whatever else makes sense. Do whatever checks are effective, given the nature of the good or service involved. You can even require the supplier to do the checks on your behalf. No matter who does it or what the criteria are, you will certainly maintain records of verifying purchased products.

Verification at the supplier's premises

The final requirement in this section relates to a rather esoteric situation that most organizations don't encounter. That is, the need to verify products at the supplier's location prior to the product being sent to your organization. This is only necessary when the product is too large, too expensive, or too critical to wait until the product shows up at your facility before you verify it. For example, airplanes are nearly always inspected at the supplier's location before they are sent to the customer. If you have products that should be inspected at the supplier's facility, then you must define the method of product verification and release in the purchasing documents. A purchase order or contract is a logical place to include such details. Many organizations won't face this situation, however.

7.5 PRODUCTION AND SERVICE PROVISION

7.5.1 Control of production and service provision

The essence of this section is process control. You must control the processes that produce your goods and services. The term "control" is very broad, but ISO 9001 is helpful enough to provide some examples of control. The final decisions of which controls are applicable to your processes are up to you.

Availability of information that describes the product

Your products must meet certain requirements. Some of the requirements are internal to your organization and some are external. Determination of product requirements is discussed in subclause 7.2.1, and the applicable portions of these requirements are what you need to make available. Document and make available the product requirements in a manner that works for you. In all likelihood, you already have specifications of some sort, especially if you manufacture product. Service providers also need to document the requirements related to their products. Take an inventory of all applicable requirements—internal, customer-mandated, legally mandated, corporate-mandated—and make sure that these are addressed. Here are some of the most typical ways to make product information available:

- Specifications
- Drawings and blueprints
- Work orders
- Travelers
- Schedules
- Contracts
- Job folder
- Production ticket

Availability of work instructions, as necessary

Work instructions are a type of procedure. The content is usually very specific, defining individual tasks and job steps. They can take many different forms: flowcharts, checklists, text procedures, diagrams, photographs, drawings. Anything that provides procedural information at a task level might be considered a work instruction. You're required to have these types of documents if you deem them necessary. The decision is yours. Here are some criteria that might help you decide if work instructions are necessary:

- *Limited training.* If personnel receive limited training, work instructions might be necessary. Simple, graphic instructions are often the most effective in these cases.
- *Infrequent tasks.* If a job is performed infrequently, it's possible that personnel may need work instructions.
- *Important tasks.* If a job is very important or high risk, it may need to be defined in a work instruction. Checklists can be an effective type of work instruction in these cases, especially when there are multiple steps that must be performed.
- *Complicated tasks.* If a job requires complicated tasks or many different process steps, a work instruction might be necessary.

Work instructions, just like all other documents, must be controlled. ISO 9001 doesn't specify where work instructions should be located, but good sense dictates that they should be as close to the job as possible.

Use of suitable equipment

This is a simple requirement. You are required to have equipment suitable to produce your goods or services. If the equipment is unsuitable, you must take action to make it suitable. These types of issues are often handled through a maintenance program of some sort, whether maintenance is performed in-house or subcontracted to outside organizations. The determination of what constitutes suitable equipment is generally determined during the planning processes described in clause 7.1.

Availability and use of monitoring and measuring equipment

The planning of processes you performed in clause 7.1 will also determine the monitoring and measuring devices you need. Whatever devices you determined as being necessary must be provided, and you must have methods for ensuring that the monitoring and measuring devices remain available. This topic is described in much more detail in clause 7.6, Control of monitoring and measuring devices (better known as calibration). Keep in mind that you're not required to have monitoring and measuring devices; they're only necessary if your products or processes require them to be effective.

Implementation of monitoring and measurement

This requirement is basically a repeat of the one above it. If you commit to monitoring and measuring something, then you must do it. The only way to prove you have done this is by maintaining a record of monitoring or measurement.

Implementation of product release, delivery, and post-delivery activities

Control must be established to ensure that you meet requirements for release, delivery, and post-delivery activities. The meaning of these words can be a little confusing. Release is how we know that a product (either a good or service) is ready to leave our direct control and be transferred to the customer. Delivery is how we actually transfer the product to the customer; in the case of a service, delivery is the performance of the service. Post-delivery might consist of installation, technical follow-up, troubleshooting, answering of questions, clarification of issues, or gathering of customer perceptions.

FREQUENTLY ASKED QUESTION

Can we use photographs as work instructions?

You can use whatever you think will communicate effectively. If you decide to use photographs, keep in mind that they will need to be controlled as documents.

7.5.2 Validation of processes for production and service provision

Validation is the method to ensure that the outputs of a process are highly predictable. Through a mix of review, control, monitoring, and qualification, we can almost guarantee that a process will produce conforming products. ISO 9001 only requires that you validate processes whose products fall into two categories:

■ Products that can't be verified, either because the technology doesn't exist or is too expensive

■ Products whose defects only become apparent after the product is in use

In these cases, you really want a process you can rely on. That's the point of validation: create a process that's so consistent that you know exactly what it will produce.

Destructive testing

In theory, destructive testing can reveal a great deal about the conformity of the product. Due to its very nature, it's expensive and only representative of a small fraction of process output. Processes that produce products that are only verifiable through destructive testing must be validated.

Examples of processes that might require validation

There are no hard and fast answers for what processes require validation. In general, the following processes are candidates for validation. The reason is that their products can't be verified, are too expensive to verify, or their defects only become known after use has started:

■ Welding

■ Brazing and soldering

■ Sterilization

- Purification
- Protective coatings and surface treatment
- Plating and anodizing
- Flame spraying
- Shot peening
- Heat treating
- Software used to perform calculations or make decisions
- Aseptic filling
- Retort food canning
- Manufacturing of implantable medical devices
- Load bearing construction
- Tunnel grouting
- Concrete compaction
- Medical decisions
- Assembly of automobile air bags
- Bomb assembly
- Processes used in the execution of criminals

Validation shall demonstrate the ability of processes

ISO 9001 doesn't provide much guidance for how process validation will be carried out. Those decisions are left up to you. The standard simply says that validation must demonstrate the ability of processes to achieve planned results. In theory, it would be a good idea to validate all processes prior to producing product. However, validation can be an expensive and time-consuming activity. Some aspects of validation can certainly be applied as the organization sees fit, even when the processes concerned produce verifiable products.

Defined criteria for review and approval of the processes

ISO 9001 requires you to define how a process will be reviewed and approved. The standard uses that "D word"—defined—which means you should give serious consideration to documenting the criteria so it's consistently communicated. Here are some typical criteria for review and approval of a process:

- *Determination of key process parameters.* What parameters are critically important in operating the process? This will differ widely depending on the nature of the process. Some key process parameters that might apply include temperature, humidity, time, pressure, speed, vibration, purity, cleanliness, and many others.

■ *Establishment of process control limits.* What are the statistical limits that indicate the inherent stability of a process? Process control limits are often applied to the key process parameters.

■ *Potential failure modes.* What could possibly fail with the process, and how likely is each failure? What should be done to prevent the failures? What should be done as a corrective measure if the failure happens anyway.

■ *Raw material requirements.* What raw materials must be used for the process to operate effectively? What are the tolerances and specifications for the raw materials? What suppliers should be used to purchase raw materials?

Approval of equipment and qualification of personnel

This clause actually mentions two different issues: equipment and personnel. Let's address one at a time. Equipment is the infrastructure that enables the process to function. It can include machinery, tools, molds, jigs, buildings, computers, and other things. You must establish the requirements around equipment. In other words, what should you verify about equipment that will enable you to have confidence in its output? Here are some examples:

■ *Equipment design.* How should the equipment be designed and constructed? What materials should be used? What special features are necessary?

■ *Calibration.* If the equipment takes measurements, then ensuring those measurements are accurate is very important.

■ *Maintenance.* Beyond calibration, what sort of cleaning, lubrication, tuning, and checking is necessary to keep the equipment working? How often should these maintenance steps be carried out?

■ *Spare parts.* What parts should be kept on hand in the event of breakdown? What is the appropriate quantity of parts? Are there special preservation requirements related to spare parts, and can we perform the preservation?

■ *Equipment manuals and troubleshooting guides.* What documentation do we need to have on-hand to effectively operate the process? Who will be responsible for ensuring we have the most current revision of documentation? (Keep in mind that this is external documentation, and you're usually relying on publications from equipment manufacturers.)

■ *Environmental conditions.* What environmental conditions are necessary for the equipment to function properly? Do you have the ability to maintain the required environmental conditions?

Qualification of personnel will address all the necessary attributes of people controlling the process. The issues addressed here will be very similar to the competency requirements described in subclause 6.2.2:

- *Training requirements.* What training is required to operate the process? Who will provide the training, and what will indicate effectiveness? What will trigger re-training?
- *Education requirements.* Do personnel require any special education, certificates, or degrees?
- *Skill requirements.* Do personnel need to possess specific skills to effectively control the process? How will skills be verified? Should skills be periodically re-verified?
- *Experience requirements.* Are there experience requirements for personnel controlling or operating the process?

Use of specific methods and procedures

Obviously, a process whose outputs can't be verified must have some specific methods and procedures. ISO 9001 doesn't explicitly require that these procedures be documented, but it would be difficult to communicate them consistently otherwise. Here are some typical methods, procedures, and documents that might be considered:

- Start-up checklists
- Standard operating procedures
- Raw material specifications
- Troubleshooting guides
- Flow diagrams of the overall process
- Emergency procedures
- Shut-down procedures
- Maintenance checklists
- Calibration procedures

Requirements for records

It would be difficult to prove validation was performed without some sort of records. Even though ISO 9001 doesn't explicitly require records here, you should define exactly what records will be maintained as part of process validation. The records will be controlled as part of your records procedures required in subclause 4.2.4. These activities related to process validation will nearly always produce records worth maintaining, such as determination of key process parameters, failure mode and effects analysis, supplier qualification results, equipment design, training and competency of personnel, maintenance, calibration, environmental monitoring, and process changes.

Revalidation

Revalidation requires that you go through the whole process from the start. Because validation can be expensive and time-consuming, you want to have a good reason for doing this. Here are some of the most common reasons for revalidating a process:

- Changes in product requirements
- Changes in key process parameters
- Shifting production to a new facility
- Environmental changes
- Changes in raw materials
- Purchase of new equipment

7.5.3 Identification and traceability

Identify the product by suitable means. Identification is one of the most fundamental controls. Confusion over "What is this stuff?" has caused more problems and customer complaints than just about any other issue. When products lack identification, you can expect trouble. It pays to have everything clearly and positively identified in some way.

This section of ISO 9001 starts with the weaselly words, "Where appropriate..." I can think of very few instances where it is appropriate to have unidentified product. Perhaps in an environment where there is only one product being produced and it is readily identifiable by sight. This is a very rare example, however. In nearly every organization it is necessary to maintain positive identification of all products, components, and raw materials. The good news is that this is very easy to do. Here are some of the most common methods:

- Labels
- Stickers
- Bar codes
- Tags
- Serial numbers
- Travelers and work orders

- Radio frequency identification
- Container identification
- Location identification

It's worth taking note of the final two examples. You could identify products by placing them in containers or physical locations that are identified. The individual products might not be identified, but their identification is communicated by where they are stored.

Identify product status with respect to monitoring and measurement

Nearly all products must be checked in some way to verify conformance. We discussed in subclause 7.5.2 that products that can't be verified, but these situations are relatively rare. You, your customers, and other parties establish product requirements, and then you monitor and measure the product to make sure it meets the requirements. This section of the standard asks you to make it clear to everyone whether the product has been monitored and measured, and what the results were. Again, this is a fairly easy discipline to carry out. Here are some examples of how it can be achieved:

- Inspection results recorded on travelers or work orders that accompany the product
- Containers that indicate the inspection status of product inside the containers
- Designated physical locations for products of different inspection status
- Test results maintained in a database that are traceable back to products by serial numbers or bar codes
- Individual inspection sheets posted on or near the product
- Inspection checklists that are traceable back to the product

As long as you can explain your process of identifying product status—and there is evidence it works—you should be in good shape.

Where traceability is a requirement...

ISO 9001 doesn't explicitly require traceability of your products. It simply says, "Where traceability is a requirement..." So when is traceability a requirement? Generally, traceability will be required under any of the following conditions:

- You require traceability as an internal requirement.

- Your customers require traceability as a term of their order or contract.
- Statutory or regulatory requirements require traceability.

Traceability is being able to say exactly what went into the product. It enables us to know what raw materials and components were used, which personnel worked on the product, and which machines and equipment were used. It always involves unique identification, because generic identification will not enable the detail needed to trace the components of a product. For tangible goods, traceability often involves batch numbers, lot numbers, and other unique identifiers. For service, traceability might be indicating who performed the service. Traceability can be indicated on travelers, work orders, job sheets, among other places (for manufacturing), and through service orders, memos, and meeting minutes (for service providers). The traceability will always involve two things: unique identifiers and records.

It's worth mentioning that there are actually two different types of traceability:

- One-way traceability: This is being able to trace backward from a product to all the things (raw materials, supplies, people, etc.) that produced the product.
- Two-way traceability: This is being able to trace back to what went into a product and being able to trace forward to where the product went when it left your control.

In general, when the term "traceability" is used without any qualifiers, it's referring to one-way traceability. If your organization defines this differently, you might want to clarify the term in your quality manual.

7.5.4 Customer property

Customer property includes a wide range of things that you use or process in some capacity, but which belong to your customer. What kinds of things might fall into this category? Here are some of the most common:

- Raw materials
- Specialized equipment
- Measuring devices
- Products returned for repair or warranty work
- Molds and tooling
- Templates and patterns
- Jigs and fixtures

■ Returnable containers
■ Packaging and labeling
■ Intellectual property

If you do use customer property of any description—and your customer has not explicitly transferred ownership of the property to your organization—you have a number of responsibilities as defined by ISO 9001.

Identify customer property

Identification means marking the property in such a way that you know it belongs to your customer. This can be accomplished in wide variety of ways. The same methods we mentioned in subclause 7.5.3, Identification and traceability, can be applied here.

Verify customer property

Verification means checking product upon arrival to make sure it meets all applicable requirements. You probably already inspect incoming material as part of complying with subclause 7.4.3, Verification of purchased product. The only difference is that you're unlikely to have a purchase order that communicates the requirements related to customer property. Establish a formal process of inspecting customer property and verifying it for all applicable requirements.

Protect and safeguard customer property

"Protect" and "safeguard" mean basically the same things. In practical terms, they mean keeping the property in good, usable condition while it's under your control. The property may require special environmental conditions, handling and storage procedures, operating conditions, or maintenance. You must agree with your customer who will be responsible for these things and how they will be performed.

Customer property that is lost, damaged, or found to be unsuitable

Hopefully, nothing bad happens to the customer property while it's in your control. However, just in case it does, you must establish a process for addressing it. If something happens to the customer property (e.g., it's lost, damaged, or broken), you must report the problem to your customer and have a record of the communication. In addition to being an ISO 9001 requirement, it's a good idea from a business standpoint.

7.5.5 Preservation of product

Preservation of product is a broad topic, and the specifics of what it might involve differ drastically from product to product. This is one of those sections of ISO 9001 that you define your own controls which are applicable. However, the standard makes it clear that your responsibility for preservation starts at internal processing (i.e., at the time you formally accept product or materials) and continues until it's delivered. Of course, you may hire subcontractors to perform delivery, but you're still responsible for their ability to preserve the product.

Preservation shall include identification

This is basically a repeat of the requirement stated in subclause 7.5.3. Refer to that subclause for guidance on product identification.

Preservation shall include handling

Handling refers to the physical manipulation of the product. You must determine the correct handling for your product, given its inherent properties and customer requirements. As usual, this will differ widely, depending on your product. Here are some examples of handling requirements:

■ Method for moving and transporting product
■ Responsibilities for moving and transporting product
■ Inspection requirements for transportation equipment
■ Limitations related to dropping or shaking the product
■ Loading patterns for shipping containers or truck trailers
■ Handling sequence
■ Handling designed to prevent electrostatic discharge (ESD)
■ Approved shippers and transportation providers
■ Hygiene requirements for personnel who handle product
■ Special handling requirements for trademarked product

Preservation shall include packaging

Nearly all physical products (i.e., goods) require packaging of some sort. The purpose of the packaging is often a mix of product preservation and loss control. If you produce goods, you probably determined the right packaging for your products long ago. Failure to do so would be very costly in terms of claims and returned goods. What you may not do is periodically re-visit the packaging requirements, based on customer feedback, changes in transportation, and changes in customer locations, etc. Determine the right packaging for your products and periodically revisit this in light of changing circumstances. It's also common for organizations to stipulate approved suppliers of packaging materials. Here are some examples of packaging requirements:

■ Outer packaging
■ Packaging graphics
■ Inner packaging
■ Labels and bar codes
■ Shrink wrapping
■ Information that personnel must record on packaging
■ Documentation attached to packaging
■ Requirements for packaging cleanliness
■ Inspection of packaging prior to use
■ Design of product packaging facilities
■ Approved method of packaging disposal

Preservation shall include storage and protection

The amount of product that gets damaged in storage is staggering. In fact, I usually consider product in stock to be a liability, as it stands such a strong chance of being damaged or compromised in some way. Nonetheless, organizations that produce goods usually have to store them for some period of time before they're shipped. ISO 9001 requires that you determine the appropriate storage and protection of these products. This not only applies to product maintained on your property, but also within subcontract warehouses and shipping facilities. You must consider the following environmental conditions when storing your product:

■ Configuration of storage area
■ Limited access to product
■ Security requirements (closed circuit cameras, locked areas)
■ Pest control requirements
■ Housekeeping requirements
■ Periodic inspection of products in stock
■ Periodic inspection of grounds and facilities
■ Location of refuse containers

- First-in, first-out (FIFO) requirements
- Monitoring of product to detect contamination

Where requirements related to identification, handling, packaging, storage, and protection are necessary, they are typically documented in work instructions, product specifications, handling standards, checklists, visual reminders, and other means. ISO 9001 does not require documented procedures, but they certainly would be a good idea to preserve the product. If your product has any special requirements, strongly consider documenting your preservation procedures in a lean and concise manner.

7.6 CONTROL OF MONITORING AND MEASURING EQUIPMENT

Control of monitoring and measuring equipment is a fancy way of saying calibration. The purpose of this element is ensuring that measuring equipment is accurate and capable of effectively verifying conformance. Calibration is the act of measuring a standard of known quality with a measuring instrument and evaluating the difference between the standard and the actual instrument measurement. All measuring equipment has a calibration tolerance, which is typically a fraction of the measurement tolerances the instrument is used to verify. So, if the measuring instrument is used to measure a product tolerance of 10 mm +/- 1 mm, then the calibration tolerance might be 10 mm +/-0.25 mm. If an instrument's measurements fall outside calibration tolerances, then it must be adjusted, repaired, or removed from use. It's important to note that measurement standards used during calibration are also measuring equipment that require periodic calibration.

Can people be calibrated?

When we talk about calibration, we are talking about devices, gages, instruments, and other physical equipment. People are not calibrated. If your organization has no measuring equipment, then this element doesn't apply to you. When personnel must be "calibrated" for consistent decision making or visual inspections, then this is accomplished through training and evaluation of competency.

Determine the monitoring and measurement to be undertaken

The first calibration requirement that ISO 9001 provides is for you to determine where monitoring and measurement takes place. This is a logical starting point. As part of planning of product realization, you probably already understand where measurements are taken. If you're not sure, take a full inventory. Here are some examples of monitoring and measurement:

■ *Product.* You probably have multiple processes for verifying product conformity. These processes may take place in a lab, quality control area, production department, or where a service is provided. When people think of calibration, verifying product conformity is usually the first thing that comes to mind.

■ *Process.* There are multiple processes within your organization that transform inputs into outputs. These processes are often monitored and measured to make sure they operate within specified parameters. Processes might be monitored for speed, accuracy, pressure, feed rate, or any other relevant characteristic.

■ *Environment.* Locations within your organization may require special environmental conditions. These environmental conditions are monitored through measuring instruments and often relate to temperature, humidity, and cleanliness. Examples of locations include laboratories, product storage areas, and sensitive work areas.

■ *Measuring instruments.* If you have measuring instruments, you may have standards for checking them. This checking may constitute calibration or may be a verification between calibrations. Regardless of what you call it, this is also a measurement process.

Determine the equipment needed to provide evidence of conformity of product

After you determine what monitoring and measuring are required, you must determine what equipment will perform the monitoring and measurement. If you're already in business, this has probably already happened through planning of product realization. Here is a sanity check, just to make certain:

■ Have we implemented measuring equipment in all areas where monitoring and measurement must occur?

■ Is the measuring equipment capable of detecting the characteristics it's being used to measure?

The second question is very important. For example, if we're measuring a product that has a dimensional tolerance of +/- 0.5 mm, we would never use a ruler that is only marked in 1 mm increments. It doesn't have the ability to detect the characteristics we're trying to measure.

ISO 9001 doesn't explicitly require a list of measuring equipment, but it can be helpful in managing the system. This list can take many forms, including a schedule, file, binder, card index, wall chart, database, or spreadsheet. The key is to consistently identify what will require calibration. Many lists of calibrated equipment will include the following bits of information for each gage:

- Serial number
- Location
- Procedure used when calibrating
- Who performs the calibration
- Last calibration date
- Next calibration date

You will likely develop your own method for identifying measuring equipment. Use the method that helps you manage your unique calibration system.

Establish processes to ensure that monitoring and measurement can be performed

You've already identified when monitoring and measurement must take place. You've also determined the appropriate measuring equipment to do the job. Now we've got to ensure the job gets done. This can be accomplished by machine programming, training, documented procedures, and other means. When people operate the measuring equipment, a mix of training and documented procedures are usually the best controls. ISO 9001 leaves the decision of how to accomplish this completely up to you.

"When necessary to ensure valid results..."

ISO 9001 starts a long list of requirements with this statement. What exactly does it mean? "When necessary to ensure valid results" means that you, your customers, or the law has established measurement requirements. Because you have committed to these requirements, the equipment being used must be accurate.

Be calibrated and/or verified

As we discussed, calibration involves measuring a standard of known quality with a measuring instrument and evaluating the difference between the known quality and the measurement from the instrument. Verification involves the same sort of checking as calibration, but it happens between calibrations. So, if an instrument gets calibrated every six months, we might verify it once a week. The point of verification is to detect small changes in an instrument's accuracy before it goes completely out of calibration. ISO 9001 requires calibration and/or verification. In practice, this means that you will at least calibrate equipment necessary to ensure valid results. You may also decide to verify the equipment between calibrations, but the choice is up to you.

At specified intervals

You must decide how often calibration and/or verification must take place. In the language of ISO 9001, these are your "specified intervals." Manufacturers of measurement equipment often establish recommended calibration frequencies for their equipment. The recommended frequency is usually a good starting point for you to use. As you learn about the reliability of the equipment in your own environment, you are free to alter it. For instance, if a manufacturer recommends its scales be calibrated every ninety days, but you have two years of data showing that it only needs it every 180 days, then you're free to lengthen the interval. The key is backing up your decisions with data. This is not an explicit requirement of ISO 9001, but a requirement of rational decision making.

When an organization decides how often each piece of measuring equipment must be calibrated and/or verified, it usually documents this in a calibration schedule. This schedule can take the form of a list, schedule, file, binder, database, spreadsheet, or any number of other approaches. The objective is that you can easily determine when devices are coming due for calibration. There are numerous software applications that can serve as calibration scheduling aids.

Against traceable measurement standards

Whatever you use as a standard for calibration must be traceable to an established source. In other words, you don't decide for yourself what makes a meter, a pound, or a gallon. You rely on a metrological source for these standard qualities. In the United States, the source for most standard measures is the National Institute of Standards and Technology (NIST). Your standards used for calibration must have an unbroken chain of calibrations back to the source. You don't have to send your standards directly to NIST to be calibrated, but if we followed the trail of what was used to calibrate them, it would lead us to NIST or another established source. It is expected that your certificates for calibration will indicate the standards used for calibration and their traceability back to the national or international source.

Occasionally, there is no standard source for a particular measurement. In these cases, the manufacturer of the measuring equipment or developer of the test will usually provide its own standard. You are required to record the basis of these standards that aren't traceable back to any national or international source. This is simply a record of where the standard came from and why no other standard exists.

Be adjusted or re-adjusted as necessary

When equipment is not within calibration or verification tolerances, it must be corrected in some way. Sometimes this can be done on the spot, and other times it requires equipment being taken out of service and scheduled for adjustment. No matter how it is accomplished, the measuring equipment can't be used while it is out of calibration. Records of calibration usually indicate the measurements obtained before and after adjustment, in cases where an adjustment was needed.

Sometimes there is a lag between the time we find out that something is out of calibration and the time we can adjust it. During this time lag, a best practice is to remove the equipment from use. Once the equipment has been adjusted to bring it back into calibration, we can reintroduce it to the work area.

Identification of calibration status

Users of measuring equipment need to know if the equipment is calibrated and ready for use. This is often accomplished through calibration stickers, but it can also be accomplished through the use of serial numbers, paint dabs, unique markings, and other means that provide traceability to the proof of calibration. The more visual and obvious the indicator, the less likely someone will use equipment that's not in calibration.

Safeguarded from adjustments that would invalidate the measurement result

All measuring equipment must be protected from unauthorized adjustments. If there is an adjustment screw on the back of the gage, for instance, access to this screw would need to be restricted. This can be accomplished with labels, wax coatings, or even training that instructs everyone to not make unauthorized adjustments.

Protected from damage and deterioration

Measuring equipment is often quite delicate and sensitive. That's why ISO 9001 requires that you protect it from damage or deterioration. There are many ways to protect measuring equipment, but here are the most common:

- Use the equipment in the manner in which it was designed, and train personnel in the correct use.
- Store equipment in the appropriate location when not in use.
- Maintain the appropriate environment for use of measuring instruments. Because of the sensitivity of many instruments, areas low in dust, grime, and extremes in temperature and humidity are usually necessary to ensure accurate results.

Assess and record the validity of previous measuring results when out of calibration

When the measuring equipment is found to be out of calibration, we have to evaluate what effect its condition might have had on previous measuring results. This can be achieved by examining how far out of calibration the gage was. If the gage was only slightly out of calibration and well within the product tolerances for the product or process it verifies, then we don't have much of a problem. If, on the other hand, the gage was very far out of calibration, then we might have to re-measure or recall our products. Whatever your decision is regarding the gage in question, you must record your decision and what action was taken. Anytime a piece of measuring equipment is found to be out-of-calibration, it should trigger an investigation into how product may have been affected.

Records of the results of calibration and verification shall be maintained

Records must be maintained for all calibrations and verifications. ISO 9001 does not specify what exactly will be included in the records, but these things are typical:

- Unique identification of the equipment
- Date of calibration

- Who performed calibration
- Results of the calibration and whether the results were within calibration tolerances
- Any necessary adjustments
- Results of the calibration after adjustment
- Unique identification of the standards used in calibration
- Calibration status of the standards used

This information is not specifically required by ISO 9001, but it is almost certainly required to provide the evidence that calibration took place. When equipment was out of calibration, remember to investigate the effect it might have had on product and process, and keep a record of this.

Confirm computer software

If computer software is used in conjunction with measuring equipment, the software must also be verified or calibrated. This is also referred to as validation. The point is to ensure that the software functions correctly and produces valid results. Most software manufacturers validate their product, and this validation can be used by your organization. Also, measuring equipment that uses software usually runs a self-check on its software each time the equipment is started. Just make sure that software is factored into the calibration if any of your measuring equipment uses software.

A calibration strategy

All the things we've discussed related to calibration are simple enough, but getting started is sometimes difficult. Here is a good generic strategy for establishing and/or improving a calibration system:

1. Take a comprehensive inventory of all measuring equipment, gages, instruments, and standards. Decide which measuring equipment is necessary to ensure valid results.

2. Create a master gage list for all the measuring equipment that must be calibrated or verified. The master gage list is your coordination tool and should be posted prominently and made available to all personnel. A database could be used in place of a list, but databases are often not understandable at a glance. The point of a list is to make the calibration process transparent and clear.

3. Establish a separate file for each piece of measuring equipment. These files are where you will maintain records on each gage. This will simplify record keeping and save you from having to dig through a huge jumble of paper when you need a calibration certificate. Don't forget to make a file for gages that are used as standards.

4. Calibrate all measuring equipment and label each with a calibration sticker (or other indicator) on it. At a minimum, the sticker should have the date the calibration was performed, who performed it, and when it's next due. In cases where a sticker is impossible, you can get creative by having the sticker in a nearby place and using a serial number to provide traceability to the record.

5. Generate a calibration record (different from the calibration sticker) for each calibration and make sure that it is maintained in the file for each of the respective gages. Make sure that your control of records procedure addresses calibration records.

FREQUENTLY ASKED QUESTIONS

We have rulers and tape measures that are used to inspect our products. Do we have to include these within our calibration process?

Yes. Any measuring instrument that is necessary to produce valid results must be calibrated.

Do we have to perform repeatability and reproducibility (R&R) studies on our measuring equipment?

ISO 9001 does not require repeatability and reproducibility studies. You only have to do R&R studies if you commit to them in your own procedures or contracts.

We have a gage that has never been out of calibration during the last three yearly calibration checks. Can we lengthen the calibration interval to eighteen months?

Yes. It's up to you to establish calibration intervals. Given that you have data showing the capability of the gage over an extended timeframe, it seems reasonable to change the interval. Consider developing a verification of the gage between the eighteen-month calibrations.

Is it OK if we use the calibration frequency of "as needed"?

No. "As needed" has no meaning as a calibration frequency. Find out from the manufacturer what is the recommended calibration frequency and consider using this as a starting point.

Chapter 6

ISO 9001 Section 8 Measurement, Analysis, and Improvement

S ection 8 is where most of the checking and improvement processes of ISO 9001 are located. It includes such things as customer satisfaction, internal audits, data analysis, corrective action, and preventive action. Whereas other parts of ISO 9001 are concerned with establishing process discipline, section 8 is concerned with changing processes to make them more effective. Many of the bottom-line benefits of ISO 9001 come from effective implementation of the requirements in section 8.

8.1 GENERAL

The title of this element says it all: general. This is another high-level section, much like all of the "dot 1" sections of ISO 9001. It repeats a lot of what clause 7.1, Planning of product realization, already requires and adds a couple of new mandates. Clause 8.1 is a "soft" element in that it rarely produces a document or record. It's simply a warm-up for what comes later in section 8. Here are some of the processes 8.1 asks you to plan and implement:

- *Processes to demonstrate conformity to product requirements.* Do you remember clause 7.1? It requires the organization to determine the verification, validation, monitoring, measurement, inspection, and test activities specific to the product. That's what the section is asking for again. If you've already determined where, when, and how, you'll demonstrate that your product meets requirements. Then you can move on to the next requirement.
- *Processes to ensure conformity of the quality management system (QMS).* The QMS is the combination of policies, procedures, and methods that enable your or-

ganization to function effectively. It has to be checked occasionally, too. That's what this requirement is asking. Make sure your QMS conforms to your requirements. This is accomplished in two ways:

☐ *Internal audits.* This is the process of verifying that you're meeting all the requirements of ISO 9001, your internal system, customers, and applicable statutory and regulatory regulations. We'll talk more about internal auditing later in subclause 8.2.2.

☐ *Management review.* This is how top management reviews data and information, and takes action to guide the organization toward success. We discussed management review in clause 5.6.

Processes to continually improve the effectiveness of the QMS

The objectives of your QMS are to create customer satisfaction and continually improve as an organization. This section is asking you to establish processes to drive improvement. Subclause 8.5.1 covers this topic in more detail, so we'll talk about it there.

Determination of applicable methods, including statistical techniques

The last part of 8.1 is quite ambiguous. What is this asking for? Are you required to have statistical techniques? The answer is no. All this requirement is saying is that you must decide if statistical techniques or other analytical methods are applicable to your operation. If you decide to use them, there are some general expectations:

■ You must use the methods correctly.

■ You must train applicable personnel in their use.

■ ISO 9001 doesn't explicitly state these requirements, but you can't effectively implement the methods otherwise.

All in all, clause 8.1 says very little that is not mentioned somewhere else in section 8 in more detail.

8.2.1 Customer satisfaction

This is a very short section of ISO 9001, but it's one of the most powerful. If implemented correctly, the customer satisfaction requirements will deliver lasting value to the organization and much customer loyalty.

Monitor information relating to customer perceptions

The key word in this requirement is "perception." A perception originates from someone's mind. It doesn't necessarily have any connection to facts or data. Perceptions are simply things you believe. Customer perceptions are especially important because customers act on the things they believe, and these actions affect your organization. Even if the perception began with a feeling that was factually incorrect, the resulting action will be a fact.

Perceptions are very broad, and certainly include both positive and negative opinions. This is why your process for capturing customer perceptions should have the ability to capture both types of feedback. Simply having a complaint process doesn't enable you to capture positive feedback. The best processes for capturing feedback use a mix of proactive and reactive methods, with the real value being in the proactive methods.

Methods for obtaining and using this information shall be determined

ISO 9001 requires that you define your methods for capturing customer perceptions. In a practical sense, this simply means that you establish the method in a consistent manner. If the method is complex or shared by many people, then "define" will usually mean "document." Whether to document your procedure is your choice. The tool you use to capture feedback will most likely be a document of some sort, at the very least.

The other half of the requirement is defining how you will use the customer perceptions. This is even more important than the gathering of perceptions. Many organizations do a good job at getting customer feedback; far fewer are good at doing something about it. You have some built-in processes for analyzing data and information within your ISO 9001 management system. The foremost is management review, discussed in clause 5.6. Management review is top management's formal review of the system and other relevant inputs and its subsequent decisions based on the data. An argument can be made for analyzing customer feedback in some place other than management review, as top management usually has too many other things to consider during that forum. Customer feedback is a very strategic type of information, and it's certainly not below the station of top management to analyze it. Here are a few of the places that customer feedback could be used and acted upon:

■ Management review
■ Business planning meetings
■ Design team meetings
■ Marketing group meetings
■ Quality assurance meetings

In many organizations, customer feedback analysis and action is the responsibility of the quality assurance team. This happens almost by default, because nobody else feels like dealing with it. Quality assurance is certainly equipped to analyze trends and take action. Customer feedback represents a huge opportunity to engage the rest of the organization in customer satisfaction. Don't make customer feedback something that is understood only by a cabal within the organization. There is nothing more important to the organization's success than customer feedback, so make it a frequent communication topic at all levels of the organization.

When action is taken on customer feedback, make sure to use your corrective and preventive action process. There's no requirement to do this, but doing so will accomplish a number of things:

■ Tracking of actions to completion
■ Clear assignment of responsibility
■ Automatic scrutiny by management review
■ Visibility to other parts of the organization

The bottom line is that customer feedback without some kind of action is worthless. Take action on the biggest opportunities and risks revealed by customer feedback, and have the discipline to follow through on what you initiate.

Because ISO 9001 leaves a lot of discretion to the organization, let's discuss the topic of customer satisfaction in more detail.

Why traditional customer surveys are a bad idea

Scaled customer surveys are among the most widely used tools in business. Unfortunately, they're also some of the worst. There's nothing evil about surveys, but they can turn an inherently simple task—such as gathering customer feedback—into something complex and unwieldy. When that happens, there's a good chance it won't satisfy its original purpose, which in this case is making improvements. Why exactly are surveys the wrong tool for most organizations? Let's explore the reasons and then consider an alternative approach that's far more appropriate.

Surveys don't produce timely data

Most traditional customer surveys are sent out periodically to a sampling of an organization's customers, typically once or twice a year. This is a manageable frequency from an administrative standpoint because implementing a survey requires a significant dedication of time and effort. The downside is that by the time the organization receives the feedback, the information is at least six months old. The information is almost worthless because customers have already acted on their perceptions before the organization has had a chance to respond. Customers don't wait around to tell you what they're going to do before they do it. If you're not tuned into your customers on a regular basis, you'll never know what hit you.

It makes more sense to gather customer feedback continually. Make the customer feedback process a continual process, not a grand event that occurs once or twice a year. This consumes far fewer resources, and it also ensures that the information is current. If you can't take action on customer perceptions within a few weeks of the perceptions being formed, there's a strong chance that you will lose your window of opportunity.

Too many questions

Another downfall of most surveys is that they try to do too much. They probe the customer experience from every imaginable angle. Although admirable, this approach results in long, unwieldy surveys that most customers run away from as fast as they can. I have gotten into the habit of scrawling "TOO LONG" in huge block letters on these kinds of surveys. I'm providing feedback, but not exactly the kind expected. Most people don't even bother to provide this much; they simply toss the long surveys into the trash.

The key to successful customer feedback is to ask about the few aspects of the customer experience that matter the most. By asking about everything under the sun, you're establishing the expectation that you'll take action on everything, which is impossible. You're also telling your customer, "Your time isn't very valuable, so the imposition of this long and boring survey should be no problem for you." Focus on a few vital issues, and these obstacles go away. The dilemma is that most organizations don't know what the few vital issues are, thus the need for long surveys. Your organization must back up and get its arms around the things that really matter to your customers.

Difficult to design

If you like defusing explosives, you'll love creating surveys. They include so many failure modes that they're nearly impossible to design correctly unless you do it for a living. Why are they so hard? Let's examine two of their more challenging aspects: questions and scales.

Most surveys comprise a series of questions or statements, followed by a response scale. The response scale usually represents degrees of satisfaction (e.g., "very satisfied," "satisfied," "neutral," etc.) or degrees of agreement (e.g., "strongly agree," "agree," "neutral," etc.). Both of these issues present huge challenges. Most people don't have the writing skills to craft clear, unambiguous survey questions. The result is that the questions don't accurately reflect the attribute that's being queried. In the spirit of getting the job done, customers will often take a guess at what the questions really mean. Like all guessing games, sometimes they'll be right and other times wrong. At best, your data will be 50-percent valid—not very good odds.

In the unlikely event that the survey questions are clear, there's still the obstacle of designing a logical response scale. This would seem to be an easy task, but it's extremely complex. Typical errors I've observed are scales that aren't balanced, scales that are biased, scales that don't have equal intervals between the points, scales that don't match the question or statement, and scales that have too many degrees of resolution. If the scale is flawed, then the data that come from it are also flawed. Garbage in, garbage out, as the saying goes.

No direction for improvement

The fourth downfall of traditional surveys is that they don't provide much guidance for improvement. Sure, they provide data, but what actions are you going to take based on those data? For example, let's imagine that you've asked customers to rate the technical knowledge of your sales force. The average response is 3.4 on a five-point scale, roughly halfway between "neither good nor bad" and "good." What does this number really mean? Even more important, what are you going to do about it? The data help you produce fancy charts, but they probably won't steer you toward specific improvements.

If you aren't able to take action on survey data, their value as improvement tools is zero. Had you asked customers an open-ended question such as, "What do you think is our biggest customer-service weakness?" you might have received some feedback that provided a clear path for improvement. In the world of customer perceptions, data don't always rule. Perceptions are by their nature qualitative and subjective, and the attempt to produce data from such a fuzzy source can be misleading. It's better simply to get actionable information than to attempt to turn human beings into precise measuring instruments. If you capture customer perceptions, analyze the trends, and take action, you've accomplished a great deal.

So, what should you do to capture customer perceptions? I've made the case that a traditional customer survey using scaled responses probably isn't the best way for most organizations to capture feedback. If not a survey, what should you do? I recommend a five-step process:

1. *Examine your existing customer interactions.* Your interactions with your customers are limitless. These contacts are conducted via telephone, e-mail, mail, fax, and in person. Because you already have numerous contacts with your customers, there's no reason to invent a new contact for the sake of collecting customer feedback. Make use of the connections you already have, and all parties will generally be much happier.

2. *Choose an interaction suited to collecting feedback.* Not all customer contacts are created equally. Certain conditions should be met when you decide which contacts will be leveraged for collecting customer feedback. In general, the contact should be neutral, routine, and candid. Here's what each of these mean:

   ■ *Neutral.* Neutral contact isn't related to an existing problem or complaint. Attempting to collect feedback when a customer already has a problem is obnoxious and counterproductive. Use an interaction that's neutral in tone and purpose, such as a query or order placement.

   ■ *Routine.* This contact happens regularly. Feedback collected from routine interactions of this sort is likely to be fresher.

   ■ *Candid.* This contact occurs between parties that trust one another and are willing to communicate freely. A candid relationship is key to collecting accurate and representative perceptions.

3. *Develop a tool that's matched to the customer interaction.* Choosing the right tool for the job is critical in every endeavor, and that goes for collecting feedback, too. Once the organization has selected an appropriate customer interaction

for collecting feedback, it must develop a tool that works in that context. This is a subjective task, and certain guidelines can assist in knowing what tools work best in different situations, such as:

- *Telephone contact.* An unobtrusive tool that's conducted at the end of a routine telephone call. Brevity is critical with this kind of tool because most people are anxious to get off the phone once their business is completed.
- *In-person visit.* A tool that enables the company to see its product in use, just as the customer experiences the product or service. The tool should also enable different people to be queried, depending on the nature of the feedback sought.
- *After service or consumption.* A tool that enables the customer to conveniently provide "flash feedback." Make the return of this feedback seamless. If the customer has to expend any effort to return the feedback, it probably won't be returned.
- *E-mail.* A live link within the body of the message that takes customers to a simple and visually appealing evaluation of their experience. Make sure the link works fast and is compatible with a variety of Internet browsers and computer monitors.
- *Benchmark customer feedback tools with other organizations.* There's no virtue in being original. Borrow good ideas and approaches as you see them. Hundreds, if not thousands, of examples exist for each of the tools described above. See what other people are doing and adapt the methods to your own needs.

4. *Focus on open-ended questions.* If you want to grab the attention of your customers, ask them what they like and don't like. It's that simple. Asking simple, open-ended questions of this sort enables customers to dictate the content of their feedback. You'll hear what's important to them. This is exactly the sort of feedback you want. Trends in open-ended feedback will keep you informed on the issues that customers care most about, something that many organizations don't understand.

Open-ended feedback also provides a clear path to improvement. Numerical ratings can help you prioritize issues, but they don't tell you exactly what to do. Open-ended feedback can. When 75 percent of your customers answer the question, "What makes you most frustrated about being our customer?" in the same way, you know exactly what you need to do to improve. There's no ambiguity.

Open-ended feedback doesn't help you make fancy charts. But do you really need more fancy charts to cover the walls of the conference room? No, you need improved customer satisfaction and loyalty. Open-ended feedback will reveal exactly what actions lead to long-term success, which is much more important than fancy charts. Here are my favorite open-ended questions. Three are about all you need.

■ Do you have any problems with our products that you haven't told us about?

■ Is there anything you think we do particularly well?

■ What could we do in the future that would make your job easier?

5. *Act on your opportunities.* Action is the most critical step of the entire process. It starts with identifying trouble areas. Problems that are revealed through feedback must be addressed immediately. This is the business equivalent of triage: Stop the bleeding and stabilize the patient. Let's hope you won't discover too many issues that require triage, but it's better to learn of these proactively while the customer is still your customer, and not a former customer.

After addressing the trouble areas, the organization must analyze the trends. Open-ended feedback follows the same rules as most traditional numerical data: It tends to clump into categories. Group the feedback into categories and apply Pareto analysis to the results. Your opportunity areas will quickly emerge. Input these opportunities into your corrective/preventive action system and track them to completion. Treat every improvement action as a mini project, with assigned tasks, responsibilities, time frames, resources, and reviews. The more sunlight shines on your improvement action, the better it will be. In other words, communicate widely. The final communication about your improvement will be to your customer: "Here's what we've done based on your feedback." These may be the most important words you ever say—and you don't have to use a traditional customer survey to say them.

FREQUENTLY ASKED QUESTIONS

Can we use our complaint program to satisfy the customer satisfaction requirements?

You can use it, but it can't be your only method of capturing customer feedback. Because ISO 9001 requires you to monitor customer perceptions, there must be a proactive aspect to your feedback to ensure the full range of possible perceptions. There's nothing proactive about waiting for customers to complain.

Do we have to capture feedback from internal customers?

The intent of this requirement is to capture the feedback of customers outside the scope of your management system. This could be another branch of your company or a different firm altogether. You don't have to capture customer feedback between departments within your organization unless you see value in it.

8.2.2 Internal audit

Internal auditing is one of the most important processes for driving improvement. During an internal audit, an organization's own employees (or personnel acting on behalf of your organization) look for evidence that you've met all relevant requirements within the scope of your management system. In the pursuit of looking where the organization has met requirements, it's inevitable that auditors will find where the organization has not met requirements. Nonconformities revealed by internal audits are treated as system issues (as opposed as personal issues) and the organization takes corrective action to ensure that the system and related process prevent the problem from happening in the future. This isn't to say that nonconformities never result from personal negligence. They do. Smart organizations strive to fix their processes so that mistakes and errors happen less often. Let's examine the specific ISO 9001 requirements of internal auditing.

Conduct internal audits at planned intervals

Audits are never a surprise. They are planned in advance, with personnel knowing exactly what processes will be covered and what requirements will apply. There are two general tools for planning audits:

■ *Audit schedule.* The audit schedule shows the audits that will take place over an extended time frame, typically six months or a year. It's available to all applicable personnel and subject to revision as circumstances change. We'll talk more about the sorts of things that could trigger a change in the audit schedule later.

■ *Audit plan.* This is a document that describes a single audit. It covers such things as the date and times of the audit; the audit scope, criteria, and objectives; who the auditors are; what areas will be covered and when; and anything else that will clarify the activity. The audit plan is provided to the auditees in advance of the audit, and it serves as a roadmap for what takes place. Like the schedule, it's subject to revision.

ISO 9001 doesn't dictate how often you must conduct audits. The universal interpretation by registrars, which is almost always in their contract for registration services, is that you will audit all processes within the scope of your management system at least once a year. When you audit an internal process, you'll address whatever ISO 9001 requirements are applicable, in addition to verifying internal procedures and policies. If an element of ISO 9001 doesn't apply to that particular department, you won't audit it in that area. Part of the audit planning process is gaining an understanding of what ISO 9001 elements apply to what departments of your organization.

Determine whether the system conforms to the planned arrangements (see 7.1)

This is one of the areas ISO 9001 says you will check during internal audits. These so-called "planned arrangements" are simply your processes for creating your product. ISO 9001 specifically mentions clause 7.1 because this is where you've planned your processes for product realization. Whether you make widgets or process insurance claims, product realization is your business's core and it will be a frequent focus of internal audits.

Determine whether the system conforms to ISO 9001

You must also verify that your system and activities conform to ISO 9001 requirements. This is often challenging for internal auditors, because it's not always clear what ISO 9001 requires. That's why this book, or some other plain-spoken reference, should be standard reading for all internal auditors. However they arrive at it, all internal auditors need to understand how the requirements of ISO 9001 relate to their own operations. This typically happens during auditor training and is reinforced by experience in applying the standard.

Determine whether the system conforms to requirements established by the organization

These are the internal procedures, policies, instructions, and other things you've committed yourself to within the scope of ISO 9001. As internal auditors, your personnel are especially well equipped to audit internal procedures, because they observe them first-hand. Part of the planning for an audit will be to determine which internal procedures, policies, and instructions relate to the audit in question. These are provided to auditors in advance to aid in their planning.

Determine whether the system is effectively implemented and maintained

This brings up the issue of effectiveness. You can meet the requirements of ISO 9001 and implement your own procedures, but still not achieve effective results. The quickest way to know if a system is effective is through the exploration of three outcomes:

■ Achievement of objectives
■ Customer satisfaction
■ Continual improvement.

If there is evidence of these outcomes, then the system can usually be said to be effective.

A documented procedure shall be established

You must document your procedure for internal auditing. As concisely and simply as possible, say how you plan, conduct, report, and record audits. Make sure to include who performs these activities. Your internal audit procedure will be the guidebook for how audits are conducted, so it needs to be very clear. If you require the use of certain tools in your audits, these should be stipulated in your procedure. Here is a summary of the issues that are typically addressed in an internal audit procedure:

■ Who maintains the audit schedule
■ Training requirements for internal auditors
■ How audits are planned and who conducts the planning

- Communication of the audit plan
- How evidence is gathered
- Guidelines for what constitutes a nonconformity
- How audit results are recorded
- Formal reporting requirements
- Corrective action on audit nonconformities
- Follow-up on corrective action to ensure effectiveness
- Review of audit results in management review

Status and importance of the processes and results of previous audits

ISO 9001 states that the audit program shall be planned, but what it's really referring to is the audit schedule. The intent is that the audit schedule is not static. You will revise your audit schedule based on two general considerations:

- *Status and importance of the processes.* This means that the parts of your organization which have higher status and importance will be audited more often. Why? Because they're more important! If these processes fail, the organization will be seriously affected. You audit them to drive improvement where it matters the most and to prevent problems. What are some of the higher status processes? This varies from one organization to the next, but these are almost universal:
  - ☐ Management review
  - ☐ Corrective and preventive action
  - ☐ Internal auditing (Yes, you will audit your internal audit process.)
  - ☐ Customer satisfaction
  - ☐ Product realization
  - ☐ Quality objectives

- *Results of previous audits.* How well or poorly a process performs in an audit will influence how often it's audited in the future. Do you know the reward for performing poorly during an audit? It's getting audited more frequently. The point is not to punish the process, but to aid in its improvement. Direct your audit resources where they're needed the most.

Make sure that your audit schedule reflects what you know about the status, importance, and audit performance of your processes.

Audit criteria, scope, frequency, and methods shall be defined

This requirement is best addressed in different places. Here is how I recommend handling each:

- *Audit criteria and scope.* The audit criteria are what you're auditing against. Typical audit criteria are "ISO 9001, the documented management system, and applicable customer requirements." The audit's scope is the departments, functions, and processes of your organization that are being audited. It's the boundaries of the audit. A typical audit scope is "Quoting, order taking, and scheduling functions at the Atlanta Regional Office." The audit criteria and scope are usually defined on the audit plan.
- *Audit frequency.* This is exactly what it sounds like. The frequency is how often different parts of your organization will be audited. The audit frequency is usually defined in the audit schedule.
- *Audit methods.* The audit methods are your procedures for carrying out audits and evaluating evidence. These are defined in your audit procedure.

Objectivity and impartiality

When you schedule and plan audits, you will strive for objectivity and impartiality. That means not assigning auditors to audit areas in which they won't be able to clearly evaluate evidence. What could possibly cause prejudice during an audit? Here are some typical causes:

- Bad relations between the auditor and auditee
- Deep friendships between the auditor and auditee
- Auditor auditing the department in which he or she works

The trick to maintaining objectivity and impartiality is having enough internal auditors. Train a team of auditors every twelve to eighteen months, and continually build your "alumni association" of auditors. Over time, you'll have a large group of past and present internal auditors to choose from, and objectivity and impartiality will never be an issue.

Auditors shall not audit their own work

Strive for objectivity and impartiality, but the bottom line is that auditors cannot audit their own work. The prior requirement sets the high bar, and this requirement sets the low bar. At the very least, you must get over the low bar (i.e., don't assign auditors to audit their own work). Here are some examples of auditing your own work:

■ Telephone operator at desk number thirteen being assigned to audit the records at desk number thirteen

■ Lab supervisor assigned to audit the lab

■ Top manager assigned to audit management review

The same strategy for achieving objectivity and impartiality (having enough auditors) will help you prevent auditors auditing their own work.

Records of the audits and their results shall be maintained

Records demonstrate a number of things: what audit planning was done, which auditors were involved, what evidence was obtained, what were the positives and negatives revealed by the audit, and what corrective actions resulted. ISO 9001 simply states that you'll keep records of audits and their results, which leaves the specifics up to you. Here are the typical records related to an internal audit process:

■ *Corrective actions.* These clearly show the nonconformities resulting from the audit. They also indicate cause(s), actions taken to address cause(s), and follow-up.

■ *Audit notes and/or checklists.* These indicate proof of the audit having taken place and provide a record of the evidence collected. If the organization maintains records of audit plans and the respective audit reports, then audit notes/checklists would not be required; the audit plans and audits reports together would provide adequate proof of the audit's occurrence.

■ *Records of auditor training, clearly showing that the auditors have met whatever competency requirements set by the organization.* These records can be maintained where other training records are maintained. As mentioned earlier, it's typical for the audit procedure to specify what training is necessary for acting as an internal auditor.

Although the following records aren't required, you should strongly consider maintaining them:

■ *Audit reports.* Many people are surprised to learn that ISO 9001 doesn't require audit reports. The standard simply requires that records be maintained of audit results. Audits reports are a recommended record because they provide a balanced of view of the entire audit: positives and negatives. They also enable a strategic summary of the audit results, which is helpful for top management to digest the results at a glance.

■ *Audit plans.* An audit plan details the hour-by-hour agenda for an individual audit. It guides the performance of the audit by telling who will do what and when.

Management shall ensure that corrective actions are taken without undue delay

This is where ISO 9001 switches gears and starts talking about what you'll do with audit nonconformities. It's a simple equation: audit nonconformity equals corrective action. You don't pick and choose which audit nonconformities require corrective action. They *all* require corrective action. If your corrective action process makes this unwieldy or difficult, it's a good idea to revisit your corrective action procedure.

The statement "without undue delay" is quite vague. In general, this simply means that corrective action will be started within a reasonable interval of the audit. It seems reasonable that corrective action could begin within a week of the audit. How long it takes to finish corrective action obviously depends on the complexity of the issue being addressed. Some audit nonconformities can be closed within a few days and others may take many months. As long as your corrective action process shows steady progress on the issues and regular reporting, there's really no time limit for how long a corrective action can be open. In most cases, the important thing is to take lasting and effective corrective action, not fast action. However, issues that affect employee health and safety often require lasting, effective, and fast corrective action.

Follow-up shall include verification of the actions taken

The final step in the audit process is verifying that management took action on the audit nonconformities. Here is what someone would typically look for when verifying action on audit nonconformities:

■ Do the actions taken relate to the identified causes?

■ Have all actions been completed?

■ Have all relevant documents been revised or written?

■ If training was part of the corrective action, was it completed?

■ Is there evidence that the causes of the nonconformity have been removed or reduced to an acceptable level?

As part of follow-up, you will record the results of actions taken. In other words, what was achieved with this corrective action? Be as clear as possible about what was determined. If a corrective action appears ineffective or incomplete, it should be resubmitted to management for more investigation and action.

Finally, keep in mind that audit results are an input to management review, as are corrective and preventive actions. The more graphic and strategic you can portray your audit results, the more they will capture the attention of top management.

FREQUENTLY ASKED QUESTIONS

Are we required to classify our internal audit nonconformities as major or minor, the way registrars do?

No. Treating all audit nonconformities as being equally important can remove a lot of controversy and confusion from the audit process.

Do we have to use checklists during our internal audit?

No. There's nothing in ISO 9001 that requires checklists for internal audits. Checklists could provide evidence that audits took place, though. They could also help guide the activities of less experienced auditors.

Do we have to audit our internal audit process?

Yes, you're required to audit all aspects of your management system, including your internal audit process.

8.2.3 Monitoring and measurement of processes

This is one of the more confusing elements of ISO 9001. Is it referring to your product realization processes (e.g., grinding, stamping, or polishing of widgets) or your management system processes (e.g., training, corrective action, or management review)? It's talking about both. You'll monitor these processes and measure them where it makes sense to do so. How critical the processes are will influence the type of monitoring and measuring applied.

Apply suitable methods for monitoring and, where applicable, measurement of processes

ISO 9001 asks that you monitor or measure your process using "suitable methods." What you consider to be suitable is based on a number of factors, including complexity of the process, process outputs, technological capabilities, customer requirements, and other factors. Here are some of the most typical methods for monitoring and measuring processes:

■ *Internal audits.* As we've discussed, internal audits verify that we're meeting all of our commitments, including ISO 9001 requirements, internal procedures, and customer requirements. Audits can be an especially effective way of monitoring a process, especially when the process doesn't produce an output that's readily measurable.

■ *Measuring process outputs.* Many processes produce a good or service. These products reveal a great deal about the processes that made them. You can certainly monitor a process through the examination of the products it produces.

■ *Process efficiency.* Efficiency indicates how well a process makes use of its resources, and is usually expressed as a ratio of inputs to outputs. So, if a key input of a process is plastic resin, then we might divide the pounds of plastic resin used by the pounds of finished product produced. As an example, imagine a process that uses 100 pounds of resin to produce ninety pounds of finished product. In this case, the efficiency is 90 percent (ninety pounds of input divided by 100 pounds of output).

■ *Visual observation.* Sometimes watching or observing a process is all that's necessary to monitor it. This is similar to auditing the process, but usually less rigorous. Sometimes visual observation of a process involves a checklist or inspection guide, which can increase the consistency of the observation.

■ *Measuring process parameters.* Many processes must meet specific parameters to operate effectively. These can include such things as speed, pressure, tension, force, temperature, pattern, program, and any number of other things. The measuring of process parameters can often be accomplished automatically, with alarms that will alert operators if the specified parameters aren't met.

ISO 9001 doesn't require you to document your methods of process monitoring and measurement. As with all other decisions related to documentation, you will weigh the risk, importance, and level of training to decide if documentation is necessary.

When results are not achieved, correction and corrective action shall be taken

Hopefully, your processes do what you planned for them to do. If you've chosen timely methods for monitoring or measurement, you should know fairly quickly if they don't achieve planned results. When processes fail to meet results, you must correct the condition and take corrective action. ISO 9001 adds the qualifier "as appropriate" to cloud the issue a bit. Basically, you get to decide when formal corrective action is needed versus doing a simple correction to the process. Just so we're all on the same page, here are definitions of the terms:

■ *Correction:* Taking action to bring the process back into planned results. Correction can usually be done quickly and often does not produce records. This is the informal route to fixing something.

■ *Corrective action:* Putting the action into your corrective action process and following all prescribed steps. Corrective action often requires a longer time frame (as opposed to something being fixed on the spot), and it always produces records. This is the formal route to fixing something.

So, when should correction or corrective action be selected? Here are some guidelines to assist in the decision. Use correction on the process when:

■ The problem is isolated and very simple.
■ The effects are insignificant.
■ The effect on customers is minimal.
■ Correction can be performed immediately.
■ The person discovering the problem is also able to correct the problem.
■ The problem is a routine part of the process.
■ There is no learning opportunity that will result from fixing the problem.
■ There is no benefit to top management hearing about the problem.
■ Changing the process to prevent future problems of this sort is not possible.

Use corrective action on the process when:

■ The problem is widespread.
■ The effects are significant.
■ Customers are detrimentally affected.
■ Correction cannot be performed immediately.
■ Investigation and determination of causes is needed.
■ Changing the process will prevent future problems.

■ There is a learning opportunity in investigating and fixing the problem.

■ Top management should hear about the problem.

■ Problems are discovered during internal audits.

As long as you can rationally defend your course of action, it's difficult for anyone to argue that you did the wrong thing. Keep in mind that corrective action is the best way to fix nonconformities in a lasting manner and have a record of what was done.

8.2.4 Monitoring and measurement of product

Most people understand monitoring and measurement of product. It's an intuitive process: check your outcomes to make sure they meet requirements. The term "monitoring and measurement of product" is a little clunky, though. More typical terms used by organizations include test, inspection, review, patrol, examination, and assessment. You're free to call it whatever makes sense to your organization.

Monitor and measure the characteristics of the product

ISO 9001 requires that you monitor and measure your product. Don't get too hung about the term "measure." The intent is that your products have requirements they must meet. The way you determine whether they meet the requirements is through measurement, even if no variable data is involved. Measurement can also take the form of attribute measures (go or no-go), which are what often results when visual inspection is applied.

The range of monitoring and measurement for products is almost limitless. Whatever reveals the true conformity of the product in the timeliest manner is what you need to implement. Here are a few of the most common ways to monitor and measure products:

■ Testing products in a lab

■ Automated monitoring by a machine

■ Operator inspection at the point of production

■ Sensory evaluation of the product

■ Comparing the product or service against a standard

■ Soliciting customer feedback of services

■ Observation of a service against defined criteria

■ Subcontracted inspection and test services

■ Relying on test data from suppliers (in the case of purchased product)

■ Sampling inspection with a statistical sampling plan

Carried out at appropriate stages

When is the right time for you to monitor and measure your product? Only you know this, and it all depends on the product and your customer's requirements. You might verify your product multiple times during its production or just inspect it once at the end of the process. The numbers and magnitude of product verifications will depend on many factors, including:

■ *Complexity of the product.* The more complex the product, the more verifications it will usually require. A wider range of verifications may also be necessary.

■ *Magnitude of product requirements.* The more requirements that have been placed on the product by customers or the organization, the more verification steps that will be necessary.

■ *Ability to detect defects.* For some products, defects become concealed as the product progress through the realization process. It makes sense to verify requirements while the defects are still detectable.

In accordance with planned arrangements

ISO 9001 states that you will carry out monitoring and measurement of product in accordance with planned arrangements. What does this mean? The planned arrangements are what you did back in clause 7.1. During planning of product realization, you began deciding what sort of verifications were needed for achieving product conformance. Here are some monitoring and measurement details that are highly recommended for organizations to define:

■ When does monitoring and measurement take place? You have already defined this as part of the "appropriate stages" above.

■ Who performs the monitoring and measurement? Be specific about what function must carry out or supervise the monitoring and measurement.

■ What type of monitoring and measurement will be used? Describe exactly what type of monitoring and measurement will take place.

■ What measuring equipment is used? This is an especially important aspect because measuring equipment usually requires calibration.

■ What are the acceptance criteria? In other words, what requirements does the product need to meet? These are sometimes referred to specifications, tolerances, or standards.

■ What records are created? When product is monitored and measured, records are always created.

It's strongly suggested that these details be documented so that monitoring and measurement of product happens consistently; however, ISO 9001 does not explicitly require documented procedures.

Evidence of conformity with the acceptance criteria/records

You must maintain records of your monitoring and measurement of product. Even if ISO 9001 didn't require this, you would need it to provide evidence that monitoring and measurement took place. Here are the most typical components of records of monitoring and measurement of product, as applicable:

- Identification of product
- Who performed or supervised the monitoring and measurement
- Who released the product (if different from who performed the monitoring and measurement)
- The acceptance criteria that was applied
- The results from monitoring and measurement of product
- Clear indication of whether requirements were met or not
- Measuring equipment used

Release of product and delivery of service shall not proceed until...

You must observe whatever product requirements that have been established. For example, you can't ship product that doesn't meet specifications. It's a no-brainer. Just abide by your procedures and specifications, and make sure you have records that demonstrate that the product has met requirements. You can get around your product specifications if your customer or another relevant authority says it's OK. This is referred to as a "concession." Concessions must meet some general conditions:

- They are always recorded.
- They are always specific about what requirements are being waived.
- They provide clear traceability to the product that they concern (dates of production, batch, serial numbers, etc.).

FREQUENTLY ASKED QUESTIONS

We inspect our products, but the record of inspection is shipped with our products to the customer. Is that OK?

No, it's not OK. How are you going to demonstrate that the inspection took place without a record of some sort? Consider developing a process that enables you to provide data to your customers and maintain proof of required inspections.

We're in a service industry, and we have customers sign-off at the end of the project that all requirements are fulfilled. Can we use this as our monitoring and measurement of product?

Yes, that would work. You are free to specify who performs monitoring and measurement of product and how it is accomplished.

Our employees do a quick visual inspection of products before they are shipped. Do we need to keep records of this?

Yes. If this is a product verification you have deemed necessary, then records of it are required. Find a simple and transparent way of capturing the record.

8.3 CONTROL OF NONCONFORMING PRODUCT

Nonconforming product is a good or service that doesn't meet requirements. The requirements can come from a variety of sources: internal requirements, customer requirements, statutory, or regulatory requirements. The purpose of controlling nonconforming products is to contain and minimize their effects. Control of nonconforming products is a close cousin to corrective action. Nonconforming products don't always result in formal corrective action, but it's always a consideration.

A system for controlling nonconformities is, by its very nature, defensive. Its purpose is to contain problems and prevent them from reaching and/or further affecting customers. Implementing a great system won't make an organization world class. On the other hand, a poor system can cause very serious problems, and possibly even lead to the organization's demise. Therefore, it makes sense to construct an effective system that everyone will use and understand.

What is a nonconforming product?

First, it may be useful to define exactly what a nonconforming product is. For such a product to exist, one or more of the following conditions must be present:

■ *Formal verification activities.* By definition, nonconforming products result from verification, inspection, or test activities. If these don't exist at a particular stage of product realization, then nonconforming products generally don't exist either. The exception is the case of nonconforming service, which is often identified through casual observation or customer feedback, as opposed to a formal inspection of any sort.

■ *Removing a product from the material flow or product realization process.* If a product's condition allows it to be handled in the normal production flow, the organization may elect to handle the product outside its nonconforming product procedures. This only works if there are formal verification activities that take place downstream in the production process.

■ *Operating conditions intended to produce conforming products.* If process conditions aren't intended to produce conforming products, the organization may handle the results of these processes outside its nonconforming product procedures. A service example might be a missed repair call because the business wasn't open. The customer who tried to schedule the repair might be irritated, but the business wasn't open at the time and the operating conditions were intended to produce products. A manufacturing example might be a production line that unavoidably produces a certain amount of start-up scrap. The scrap is simply part of getting the process up to normal operating conditions. The organization could elect to handle this product outside of its procedures for nonconforming products, especially when the scrap or waste in no way resembles conforming product. Trouble arises when the scrap or waste looks exactly like conforming product, as it does in many industries, such as chemical manufacturing. In these cases, potential misidentification outweighs other factors and makes nonconforming product procedures a necessity.

■ *Risk to the organization.* Regardless of any other considerations, an organization can decide that the business risk or potential liability is great enough to treat products as nonconforming at any particular stage of the process. Regardless of ISO 9001 requirements, this is the category that matters most when deciding if something is nonconforming.

Even given these guidelines, an organization may discover a considerable amount of gray area regarding what is or isn't nonconforming product. This is only natural and a reflection of the real-life complexities of business. The organization must look objectively at its own operations, analyze its unique risk factors, and decide what will be included within its system for nonconforming products. Some situations will be quite obvious, and others won't.

Identifying nonconforming products

The first requirement for nonconforming products in ISO 9001 states that product which doesn't conform to product requirements is identified and controlled. The two key words here are "identification" and "control." Let's address identification first.

Simply put, an organization must identify products that don't conform to requirements. This is an extension of the requirement for identifying all products by suitable means throughout product realization. Everything must be identified. However, the standard doesn't prescribe any particular methods of identifying nonconforming products. Indeed, it can take many forms, all of which have their place:

- ■ Identification of nonconforming goods:
  - ☐ Tags, signs, or labels affixed to the product
  - ☐ Labeled bins, boxes, and bags
  - ☐ Remarks or descriptions written directly on the product
  - ☐ Tape or ribbon wrapped around the product
  - ☐ Paint spots or other coded markings on the product
  - ☐ Electronic identification, often by means of a barcode affixed to the product
  - ☐ Storing the product in specially marked areas

- ■ Identification of nonconforming services:
  - ☐ Work order notated with problems that occurred during a service call
  - ☐ Note stapled to a customer receipt
  - ☐ Completion of a nonconforming service report
  - ☐ Chalkboard, grease board, or bulletin board with details about nonconforming services
  - ☐ Intranet page, database, or spreadsheet with details about nonconforming services

Identification of nonconforming goods typically involves visible identifiers on or near the good. Identification of nonconforming services, on the other hand, usually involves records that are tied to a job or transaction.

The organization is responsible for deciding which forms of identification are most appropriate for its manner of operations. No universal conventions exist for what nonconforming identification should look like. Is a green "rejected" tag OK? Sure, if that's what the organization wants to use. How about the words "service failure" scrawled in crayon on the work order? No problem. The identification system needn't be conventional. What's important is that it's effective and understood by users.

Controlling nonconforming products

Control is the next issue ISO 9001 requires organizations to address, and it encompasses a wide range of potential activities:

■ Establishing special handling requirements
■ Segregating goods from conforming products
■ Securing goods in locked or protected areas
■ Establishing documented procedures
■ Defining responsibilities and authorities
■ Training employees on procedures
■ Defining timeframes for taking action
■ Defining dispositions
■ Recording nonconformities
■ Connections to the corrective action system

In other words, "control" summarizes all the methods that lead to two desired outcomes: preventing nonconforming products from reaching and/or further impacting the customer, and eliminating the causes of nonconforming products. Identification is actually a component of control, although the standard treats it separately. The specific means of control used by an organization will be described in a documented procedure.

Documented procedure

The next requirement stipulated by ISO 9001 is that controls and related responsibilities and authorities for dealing with nonconforming product be defined in a documented procedure. This requirement is self-explanatory. Try to make this procedure simple and concise. How complex is your system for controlling nonconforming products? Probably not very. Ensure that the documented procedure is equally uncomplicated. The organization might consider using graphic explanations, such as flow diagrams, to make the procedure more intuitive and user-friendly.

Responsibilities and authorities must be defined clearly in the documented procedure for each stage of control. Consider the following issues within the procedure:

- Who can identify nonconforming goods or services?
- Who can move or handle nonconforming goods?
- What kind of communication should take place about nonconforming products?
- Who can authorize disposition of nonconforming goods or services?
- Who can carry out the disposition?

These responsibilities and authorities should be addressed in a no-nonsense manner, and the persons who have responsibilities and authorities within the system should receive appropriate training. Defined responsibilities and authorities are useless if nobody knows about them.

Dispositioning nonconforming products

ISO 9001 next addresses dispositioning of nonconforming products. Simply stated, dispositioning means deciding what to do with nonconforming product. ISO 9001 offers four possible dispositions:

- *Taking action to eliminate the detected nonconformity.* The key word here is "eliminate." The product may maintain its basic identity as a product, but the nonconformity will be eliminated. This can occur in a variety of ways:
  - ☐ By re-performing the service and correctly provide the desired service, either in whole or in part.
  - ☐ By repairing the good. This includes actions that make the product functional, although it doesn't conform perfectly to the original requirements. Such a product may not carry the same warranty as first-quality products.
  - ☐ By reworking the good. Actions that make the product conform to the original requirements. In the customers' eyes, this product is exactly the same as a first-quality conforming product.
  - ☐ By reprocessing the product and sending it back through the transformation process. This is done in many continuous process industries, such as chemicals and plastics.

Authorizing its use, release, or acceptance under concession

In this case, the product still doesn't meet requirements. Nothing has been done to eliminate the nonconformity or alter the good or service's quality. However, somebody has decided to use, release, or accept the product anyway. If a product is nonconforming according to the organization's internal specifications but acceptable according to the customer's specifications, a concession can be issued by the organization. However, if the product is nonconforming according to the customer's specifications, the concession can only come from the customer.

The term "concession" may cause some confusion. It's nothing more than an agreement to use, release, or accept a product. Concessions are always recorded; otherwise, they're worthless. If no record of the concession exists, then the organization has nothing to stand behind in the case of later disputes. Moreover, ISO 9001 requires concessions to be recorded.

Concessions normally include the following details:

- The condition or quality level that has been accepted
- The identification of the good or service that is covered under the concession
- The person who has authorized the concession, including a signature, if possible
- The date and time the concession was granted

These could be recorded on the original sales order, the customer's purchase order, internal quality assurance records, or other relevant documentation. Regardless of where and how the concession is recorded, the important thing is that it's clear and unambiguous.

Taking action to preclude its original intended use or application

This disposition can lead to a number of different actions. Ultimately, the product isn't going to be used or applied as it was originally intended. This normally occurs through one of the following actions:

- *Scrapping.* This action actually gets rid of the product, such as tossing it into a dumpster.
- *Discontinuing.* In the case of a service, we may determine that we're unable to meet requirements and a refund is issued.
- *Recycling.* The product is sent to an outside party that can recycle the product or its components into something usable

- *Reprocessing.* The product is changed into something entirely different from what was originally intended.
- *Re-grading.* This is possible when the good or service was nonconforming according to one set of requirements, but it conforms to a lesser or different set of requirements.
- *Controlled destruction.* Some products are especially sensitive and can't be simply scrapped. They must be destroyed, with proof of their destruction, to ensure they don't fall into the wrong hands. Products of this sort might include trademarked materials, dangerous products (such as adulterated food or out-of-spec tubing from a nuclear power plant), and potentially unsafe products (such as nonconforming aircraft parts).

Taking action when nonconforming product is detected after delivery or use

Occasionally—but hopefully not often—nonconformities will be detected after delivery or after the customer has used the product. ISO 9001 requires that the organization take action appropriate to the effects or potential effects of the nonconformity. This can mean a number of things. Typically with goods, organizations institute a returned goods process to deal with nonconformities that are detected after delivery or use has begun.

For most goods, this system works fairly well and follows this general sequence:

1. The customer contacts the organization to report the nonconformity.
2. If it's determined to be appropriate, the customer is issued a tracking number of some sort. This number is often referred to as returned materials authorization (RMA) or returned goods authorization (RGA).
3. The customer is asked to mail or ship the product back to the organization, referencing the assigned tracking number.
4. When the product returns to the organization, it's handled much like any other nonconformity. The primary difference is that there may be the additional issue of crediting the customer for all or part of the product's cost.
5. Corrective action may be initiated to determine and eliminate the root cause of the nonconformity, as with in any other nonconforming product situation. The key benefit of a returned goods process is that the organization can see the nonconformity for itself, rather than just hearing about it.

Sometimes the effects of the nonconformity may require more or less action than the returned goods process described above. For wide-ranging or potentially harmful nonconformities, the organization may institute a universal recall of all products sold within a certain time period. For very small nonconformities, the customer may simply receive an automatic credit and be asked to discard the nonconforming product. In any case, the organization must consider the nonconformity's effects and take action that logically matches those effects.

In their procedures for controlling nonconforming products, some organizations stipulate time limits within which a disposition must be accomplished (e.g., "Nonconforming products must be dispositioned within thirty days of being identified."). However, common sense dictates that some dispositions may take longer to arrive at than others. Time limits are rarely a good idea, and they usually result in the organization violating its own procedures. If organizations want to reduce the amount of time between identification and disposition, managers simply need to monitor products in their nonconforming areas, a responsibility that is often ignored.

Records

ISO 9001 requires that records be maintained that describe the nature of nonconformities along with any subsequent actions taken. This requirement has given people a lot of heartache: "We're going to spend all our time filling out records!" The truth is that if an organization has that many nonconformities, completing records is the least of its problems.

At least the first three of the following pieces of information must be recorded:
- A description of the nonconformity
- Action taken, otherwise known as disposition
- Re-verification (i.e., when the nonconformity has been corrected)
- Details of concessions, if any

Because we've already discussed documenting the concession, let's focus on the other three items. The description of the nonconformity and action taken can easily be recorded on the form that identifies the product as nonconforming. Keep it simple. Like most paperwork, the more complex a record is, the less employees will use it. The best option is electronic record keeping, particularly for organizations that identify nonconforming products through barcodes or other electronic means.

Re-verifying nonconforming products

When nonconforming products are corrected, they must be re-verified. This verification must match the original requirements that the product was intended to meet—otherwise, you've re-graded the product. Re-verification can be done through the original inspection process or by a completely different function—it doesn't matter. The important thing is that the re-verification is recorded, just like any formal verification.

Two elements must be included in this record:

■ Evidence of conformity with acceptance criteria (i.e., actual measurements or observations)

■ Identification of the person authorizing the release (i.e., the person performing the verification or responsible for seeing that the task is performed)

The re-verification record can be kept anywhere that makes sense to the organization. The only imperative is that the relevant people know where it is and can retrieve it.

Connection to corrective action

Do all instances of nonconforming products result in corrective action? This is a very good question, and the answer requires some interpretation. The ISO 9001 requirements for corrective action are straightforward: "The organization shall take action to eliminate the causes of nonconformities in order to prevent recurrence." This basically means that all nonconformities will be submitted for corrective action, but the very next sentence provides something of a trap door: "Corrective actions shall be appropriate to the effects of the nonconformities encountered." My interpretation is that "appropriate actions" can include anything from companywide initiatives to no action at all. It all depends on the effects of the nonconformities. In other words, the organization must evaluate, among other considerations, the organizational risk and potential impact on customer satisfaction, and then take action that logically fits the description of "appropriate." As long as there's evidence that the organization has performed this evaluation and has an objective basis for its action—or nonaction—then nobody should object.

Keep in mind that the corrective and preventive action system is worthless if it's not used. An organization should look for every possible opportunity to put it to use and enforce causal investigation into nonconformities. Clearly, the link between corrective actions and control of nonconforming products is one of the most critical relationships within any management system. In the end, your system for controlling nonconforming products will be fatally flawed if it doesn't include a clear and direct connection to your corrective action system.

FREQUENTLY ASKED QUESTIONS

Nonconforming products costing more than $500 are handled through our formal procedure. Nonconforming products of smaller values are handled at the employee's discretion. Is this OK?

No. The requirements of this section address all nonconforming products, not just certain categories. If you design a lean and concise process for nonconforming products, then there should be no problem applying it to all manner of products.

We use customer feedback as a way to identify nonconforming service. We don't make and inspect a tangible product, so we feel this is one of the best ways to identify problems. Will this work?

Yes. Applying these requirements to a service organization will take some creativity, and this sounds like a perfectly reasonable way to do it. Keep in mind that your internal checks of service work might also identify nonconformities.

8.4 ANALYSIS OF DATA

There is no shortage of data in most organizations. The proliferation of computers has made the collection of data remarkably easy. What organizations often neglect is the analysis of data. What do all these numbers mean and what should we do about them? Data collection is easy; analysis of data is much harder. Of course, it's the analysis that delivers the value.

ISO 9001 doesn't specify how or where analysis of data will take place. It's up to the organization to make these decisions, and there are plenty of management system processes that will facilitate data analysis. One particularly good process for analysis is management review. The entire purpose of management review is to analyze data, make decisions, and take action to improve. With a little planning, all the data required by clause 8.4 can be addressed during management review. This is only the low bar, of course. There are many more places and people who can be involved in the analysis of data. The more people who are involved, the better the organization's decision making will become.

Let's examine the four types of data you're required to analyze.

Data on customer satisfaction

We discussed customer feedback in subclause 8.2.1. This is exactly the sort of data ISO 9001 is asking you to analyze. The data can be trends, percentages, averages, outliers, or individual comments. Strive to consolidate data into categories, and show the categories as graphical representations: charts, graphs, and diagrams. The more your customer feedback can be converted to graphics, the easier it will be to interpret. And remember that analysis without action is worthless, especially when it comes to customer feedback. Collect it, analyze it, and take action to improve it.

Here are some particularly useful types of customer satisfaction data:

■ Biggest complaints categories
■ Most frequently desired features
■ Positive comments and praise
■ Most important product attributes
■ Biggest product strengths
■ Complaints per million dollars in sales
■ Specific ideas and suggestions
■ Response rates from customer feedback tools
■ Improvements to the process for capturing feedback

Data on conformity to product requirements

You have multiple ways of verifying the conformity of your products, and the verification always results in a record. ISO 9001 is asking you to mine these records for information about how well your products meet requirements. As with all data, trends and graphical depictions facilitate interpretation.

Here are some useful categories of product conformity data:

■ In-process inspection rates
■ Final inspection rates
■ Types of product defects
■ Products with the highest and lowest rates of nonconformity
■ Trends in return and warranty rates
■ Test data

- Product audit results
- Process capability against specifications
- Performance against project plan
- On-time delivery rate
- Service effectiveness
- Jobs completed according to schedule
- Customer feedback on service transactions

Characteristics and trends of processes and products

This is a broad, catchall category of data that can mean almost anything. Do you have any data on characteristics and trends? Certainly you do. Some of the data we've already discussed falls into this category. Here are some other examples:

- Trends in audit results
- Process improvements
- Product enhancements
- Trends in corrective and preventive actions
- Progress against objectives
- Process performance against requirements
- Regulatory conformance
- Safety performance
- Effectiveness of training
- Employee suggestions
- Employee recognition opportunities

Supplier data

We've already discussed the requirements of evaluating your suppliers (sub-clause 7.4.1). Now you've got to analyze the data. If you establish meaningful criteria for evaluating suppliers, this requirement will be easy to satisfy. Here are some typical types of supplier data:

- Trends in pricing
- On-time performance
- Conformity of products
- Responsiveness to inquiries and requests
- Corrective actions taken by suppliers
- Supplier audit performance
- Supplier solvency and viability

- Knowledge of supplier personnel
- Candidates for supplier awards
- Supplier management system certification
- Supplier internal audit results

Proof of data analysis

It's virtually impossible to prove that you analyzed data without some sort of records. ISO 9001 doesn't require records here, but I don't know how else conformity could be demonstrated. The good news is that records should be easy to produce. Here are some records that would generally indicate analysis of data:

- Management review records
- Staff meeting minutes
- Problem-solving team records
- Corrective actions that result from analysis of data
- Preventive actions that result from analysis of data
- Memos and e-mails related to data analysis
- Charts and graphs notated with analysis results

8.5.1 Continual improvement

Continual improvement is the process of becoming a more effective organization. It's an incremental process, meaning you'll take many small steps toward improvement. Huge breakthroughs would be nice, but the reality of business is that there are only so many big wins out there. The trick is to put processes in place that will drive improvement across a wide swath of your organization, involving as many people as possible.

ISO 9001 requires continual improvement of the quality management system. Any organization that is currently in business should have no trouble finding some evidence of improvement within its operation. If you are using the prescribed tools, continual improvement will become almost automatic. The required tools include:

- *Quality policy.* This document provides the organization's commitment to quality and gives general direction on what the organization hopes to achieve. The quality policy facilitates continual improvement by letting everyone know where the organization is headed in general terms. As an organization, do we care about innovation or cost reduction? Do our customers value us because of speed and efficiency, or prestige and luxury? The policy establishes the themes that are at the core of our organization, and these themes are generally where improvement efforts are aimed.

■ *Objectives.* These are the measurable indicators of whether the organization is moving in the correct direction. Whereas the quality policy puts forth general themes, the objectives are very specific. Objectives are communications tools that tell everyone how we will measure success. Objectives matched with specific action plans create an engine for driving the organization forward.

■ *Audit results.* Audits reveal where the organization meets and fails to meet requirements. When corrective action is taken on the nonconformities, improvements inevitably result. Audits also serve as an involvement tool, engaging employees in the improvement of the organization in ways they otherwise would not be able to realize.

■ *Analysis of data.* Data can reveal opportunities, threats, risks, and untold other things. The trick is to make data analysis systematic: a transparent part of the way you do business. Conversion of data into graphics and simple statistics can facilitate its interpretation and analysis. As we mentioned earlier, management review can serve as a convenient forum for analyzing data and making decisions based on the analysis.

■ *Corrective and preventive actions.* These are the systematic processes for investigating and removing the causes of actual and potential problems. These processes are among the most fundamental for making continual improvement a reality. By keeping your corrective and preventive action processes simple, streamlined, and timely, you're more likely to get people involved and produce improvements.

■ *Management review.* This is where top management reviews the organization's results and the output of the management system to determine where further improvements can be made. It's one of the most important processes in the entire management system. Far from being a "dog and pony show," the intent is to truly analyze trends and data, and decide what actions should be taken to drive the organization forward.

Although you are required to continually improve the quality management system, you are strongly encouraged to improve the overall performance of your organization. In fact, there's little point in improving the management system if it does not in turn improve the organization's overall performance, efficiency, and effectiveness. Strive for the higher standard of improvement, and you'll be sure to at least hit the mark required by ISO 9001.

FREQUENTLY ASKED QUESTIONS

Do we need to establish a stand-alone continual improvement program?

No, there is no need to establish a stand-alone continual improvement program. As long as you're using your other improvement processes correctly (quality policy, quality objectives, audit results, analysis of data, corrective and preventive actions, and management review), then together they constitute your continual improvement process.

Can we use our Six Sigma program to satisfy the continual improvement requirements of ISO 9001?

Yes, of course. Just make sure you're also using the other improvement tools mentioned by ISO 9001.

I am often asked how other improvement methods and tools connect to ISO 9001. The answer is that they build on the basic control and process discipline that ISO 9001 establishes. ISO 9001 provides a way to sustain improvements that result from an organization's efforts. A common weakness is that an organization makes an improvement, but lacks the planning, communication, and document control to sustain the improvement. With time, it fades away. ISO 9001 is the foundation on which nearly any improvement methodology can be built, including:

■ Six Sigma
■ Lean enterprise
■ Malcolm Baldrige National Quality Award Program
■ Statistical process control
■ Total quality management
■ Natural work teams
■ Balanced scorecard
■ And many others

It's foolish to embark on any improvement efforts when you don't have the system to keep it going. ISO 9001 provides that system.

8.5.2 Corrective action

Corrective action is the process for investigating and taking action on existing problems. It is one of the most fundamental of management system processes. An organization that can't solve its problems effectively is an organization that won't be in existence for very long. ISO 9001 provides a set of basic steps to be carried out in the solving of problems.

What sorts of problems might trigger corrective action? Any problem within the organization is fair game. In fact, the wider the system is applied, the better. Here are some examples of issues that you could address through your corrective action system:

- Customer complaints
- Internal defects and errors
- Process inefficiencies
- Supplier problems
- Audit nonconformities
- Returned goods
- Safety incidents
- Environmental problems
- Employee ideas and feedback
- Service delays

Any activity, process, or product that does not meet requirements is subject to corrective action. Generally, corrective action is nothing more than a system for breaking a large issue into smaller, manageable pieces. It's project management at its simplest.

Eliminate the causes of nonconformities

ISO 9001 makes it clear that the ultimate objective of corrective action is to eliminate the causes of nonconformities. First, we must find the causes, and then we must eliminate them. Very rarely is there a single root cause to any problem. More often, problems are caused by a chain of interrelated causes that all must be identified and addressed. Organizations often do a very poor job of identifying causes. Either through ignorance or laziness, these bogus causes often appear on corrective action reports:

- Employee error
- Failure to follow procedure

- Not paying attention
- Sloppy work
- Unknown
- Personnel oversight

These are bogus causes because they are all person-centered, as opposed to being process-centered. If we desire true improvement of the process, we must dig deeper to find out why the employee made the error. There was some flaw in the process that enabled the employee to make an error. We must investigate each step of the process and issues that could lead to our problem, including:

- Missing or obsolete information
- Inadequate tools
- Unclear instructions
- Procedures that are flawed
- Customer requirements that aren't understood
- Needless complexity
- Conflicting goals
- Incompatible instructions from multiple sources
- Ineffective training

Try to identify all the existing and potential causes to the problem at hand. Even though ISO 9001 uses the term "eliminate the causes of nonconformities," the truth is that not all causes can be removed. However, nearly all causes can be reduced. Remove or reduce all the identified causes to an acceptable level and your corrective action will have been a success.

Appropriate to the effects of the nonconformities encountered

ISO 9001 also tells us that corrective action must be appropriate to the effects of the nonconformities encountered. This means that big problems get big solutions, and little problems get little solutions. It gives us the discretion of applying appropriate fixes. Sometimes, we decide not to apply a fix because the effect of the nonconformity is negligible. This is not a loop-hole to allow organizations to avoid facing their problems. It's simply a common sense statement of directing your resources where they are most needed. You could do nothing but solve problems twenty-four hours a day, but not all problems are created equal. Attack the ones that have the most bearing on your success and follow through all the way to completion.

Documented procedure

You must define your corrective action process in a documented procedure. It's common for organizations to address preventive actions in this same procedure since the two topics are so closely related. Your organization's problem-solving method, if you have adopted one, is also a logical topic to address with this procedure. Here are some topics that would add value to any corrective action procedure:

■ Who can initiate corrective action?

■ Who must approve a corrective action?

■ How the details of problems must be recorded?

■ Tools that should be used as part of corrective action

■ The mechanism for tracking corrective actions through the process

■ Who assigns responsibility to investigation and action?

■ Follow-up to determine the results of actions taken

■ Recording and reporting requirements

■ Connection to management review

Here are the topics that ISO 9001 specifically requires to be addressed within your corrective action procedure:

■ *Review nonconformities (including customer complaints).* You must develop a process for how nonconformities are reviewed. A better term than "reviewed" would be "investigated." Most organizations assign each corrective action to an individual whose responsibility it is to investigate the issues surrounding the nonconformity. It's difficult to hold committees accountable, but it's easy to hold individuals accountable. The assigned person acts as the project manager for the investigation and resulting action, driving the process and recruiting other participants as necessary. The so-called project manager for a corrective action is typically the person who has the most in-depth understanding of the variables involved, although the responsibility could be assigned to anyone.

■ *Determine the causes of nonconformities.* This is one of the most critical steps in the corrective action process. It's almost impossible (except through luck) to take effective corrective action on a problem unless you have determined the cause. It may be helpful if you provide some guidance on how causes are determined within your procedure. We talked about problem causes earlier in this section. Don't be afraid of sending corrective actions back to their owners when the identified cause is clearly superficial or incorrect.

Training may be required to encourage better cause investigation. One option is to hold a short course in root cause analysis and problem solving. This course could easily be designed and presented in-house, but there are also plenty of course providers who would be happy to do it for you for a fee. Topics might include:

- [ ] What exactly is a problem cause versus a symptom?
- [ ] What are the techniques for determining causes?
- [ ] What are typical steps for problem solving?
- [ ] What analytical tools are appropriate at each stage of problem solving?
- [ ] How do you conduct an effective meeting?
- [ ] How do you manage team dynamics in a problem-solving environment?
- [ ] How can conflict be effectively managed?

■ *Evaluate the need for action.* Once you have determined the causes, you may or may not decide to take action. The reason is that some causes are extremely expensive or difficult to remove. The opposite is also true: some causes are inconsequential. If the effect of the problem is relatively small, you can logically decide not to take action. However, when you do take action, your action must be aimed at making sure that nonconformities don't recur.

■ *Determine and implement necessary actions.* Decipher what actions are necessary to remove or reduce the causes of the problem, then make sure that the actions get implemented. This is the project management aspect of corrective action. Keep in mind that some fixes are actually a combination of many smaller fixes. Manage the process with persistence and discipline.

■ *Record results.* After taking action, you must figure out what your actions have resulted in. Does evidence indicate that the causes have been removed or reduced? If evidence doesn't indicate that the causes of the problem have been removed or reduced, then the actions did not achieve their objectives. Send it back for rework.

It's worth mentioning that this step is the only one with corrective action that specifically requires record keeping. The reality is that all of the steps must be recorded to demonstrate that you have met the intent of this element.

■ *Review corrective actions.* Corrective and preventive actions are explicit inputs to management review. The intent is that you discuss the overall trends and areas that require top management's attention. Because the corrective and preventive action process is one of the most important in the entire management system, it's critical that top management understand whether the process is producing effective results.

FREQUENTLY ASKED QUESTIONS

We have separate procedures for each type of corrective action. We have one for supplier corrective actions, one for audit corrective actions, and another for customer complaints. Is this OK?

Yes. Structure your corrective action process in whatever way makes the most sense to you.

Some of our corrective actions have been open for more than six months because they involve capital investments. Is it OK for them to remain open so long?

Yes. As long as you're making progress on the actions and updating the records, there's no problem at all.

8.5.3 Preventive action

Preventive action is very similar to corrective action, except that in the case of preventive action the problem has not yet occurred. For that reason, preventive action is considerably more difficult than corrective action. It requires that you be able to look into the future. You must sniff the wind, so to speak, and predict when something bad might happen in the days, weeks, or months ahead. This is quite a feat.

What sorts of things might trigger preventive action? Here are a few:

- Analysis of data
- Review of trends
- Statistical process control
- Management review
- Employee ideas and inputs
- Customer feedback and suggestions
- Market research
- Strategic planning

The reality is that your organization is already taking preventive action. The competitive environment requires it. What is probably not happening, though, is the application of a systematic approach to preventive action. It happens informally. Records aren't generated either. The trick is convert this informal activity into something disciplined that builds a culture of organizational improvement. When opportunities arise, input them into your preventive action process. This isn't just for the purpose of satisfying ISO 9001 requirements; it's for building a repository of organizational knowledge and for enforcing a degree of consistency around improvement efforts.

ISO 9001 requires that you define your preventive action process in a documented procedure. As I stated earlier, it's very common to combine these procedures with the ones for corrective action. The required issues to be addressed by the procedure are the same as the ones related to corrective action, e.g., determining causes, evaluating need for action, etc. However, the focus will be on preventive action.

The heart of preventive action is the ability to analyze data and draw reasonable conclusions. A natural source of preventive action is your management review function. In that process, top managers are reviewing and analyzing strategic data. If this is done in a thoughtful manner, it will be almost impossible to avoid taking preventive action. Of course, there are many other sources of preventive action. Preventive action is happening all the time, just not in a systematic and recorded manner. Take the time to record the output of your preventive actions and you'll have met the intent of this requirement.

FREQUENTLY ASKED QUESTION

Does a preventive action have to come from a potential nonconformity?

No. A preventive action can originate from just about any source: a potential nonconformity, employee suggestions, customer feedback, or analysis of trends, to name just a few. ISO 9001 mentions preventive actions being taken to eliminate the causes of potential nonconformities, but this is only a starting point.

Chapter 7

Conclusion

I f you have read this far, you probably have a strong understanding of ISO 9001. Now your challenge is spreading this understanding throughout your organization. After all, it's not good enough that one person, or even a small group of people, understand the intent and application of ISO 9001. Everybody plays a role and everybody needs to know what he or she is getting into. You could hand out copies of this book and make everybody read them, but it's more likely that you will have to take on the role of coach and educator. You'll be the disciple that spreads the word, so to speak.

What should you keep in mind as you spread the word about ISO 9001? Here are some key points to remember:

■ *Focus on the applicable portions of ISO 9001.* Emphasize the requirements of the standard that relate to different people's jobs. For example, not everyone needs to understand the requirements for evaluating suppliers. Give people the right message for the job they are doing.

■ *Use examples that people understand.* Even a plain English presentation of ISO 9001 will fall flat without some living examples. Paint the picture of what the management system relates to in your organization. So, if you're talking about calibration, list the measuring instruments that your organization uses and explain how they are currently controlled.

■ *Remember that some topics are universal.* There are a number of management system aspects that apply to everyone, from one end of the organization to the other. These include the quality policy, quality objectives, document control, and document access. There may be additional universalities, too, depending on the nature of your organization.

■ *Highlight concrete benefits.* Tell people in no uncertain terms why ISO 9001 is worth implementing. Explain the specific benefits of different parts of the standard, and illustrate the types of problems that can be prevented. Remind everyone (diplomatically) of problems that have taken place in the organization, and connect these problems to the lack of systems and consistent processes.

■ *Be enthusiastic.* Believe in the benefits of ISO 9001. Internalize the message and be prepared to *sell* it to everyone. All successful messages have an element of selling. When people can see your passion, they become believers themselves.

■ *Involve people in the implementation.* The more people who are involved in ISO 9001 implementation, the more people who will feel a sense of ownership in the system. Broad ownership will help drive the success of your management system.

■ *Develop your own language.* The term ISO 9001 can turn a lot of people off. So why even use it? If there's a chance that certain words will prejudice people against the management system, then use different words. Go through the standard and identify words that will confuse or turn people off in your organization. Replace these words within your quality manual with terms that have more positive meaning. ISO 9001 might become the ACME improvement model and quality objectives might become key measures. Get creative.

■ *Engage top management early and often.* Your first training session on ISO 9001 needs to be with top management. So does your last training session. Engage top management with early action items like the development of your quality policy and quality objectives, and keep them abreast of all developments involving other people. Encourage top management to communicate their interest and belief in the management system.

■ *Build on the basics of ISO 9001.* The standard provides fundamental management systems, but it is by no means comprehensive. Once you have implemented the basics, look toward other improvement methodologies (Six Sigma, Malcolm Baldrige, etc.) that will complement your management system. The ISO 9001 disciplines will enable you to sustain your improvements.

Now get out there and help your colleagues understand ISO 9001 in plain English. The standard is a great model for success, as long as everybody understands what it requires.

Index